THE STANDARD DEVIANTS® STUDY SIDEKICK

STUDY SIDEKICK

THE ROCKIN' WORLD OF GEOLOGY PARTS 1&2 STUDY SIDEKICK (1ST EDITION)

Written by The Standard Deviants® Academic Team, including:
Dr. Julia Sykes-Nord, Ph.D.
Kristie Wingenbach

Edited by:
Rachel Galvin

Contributing Editors:
Dr. Janet Herman, Ph.D.

Graphic Design by:
C. Christopher Stevens
Sarah Fry

800-238-9669
e-mail: cerebellum@mindspring.com
www.cerebellum.com

THE STANDARD DEVIANTS™

OTHER SUBJECTS FROM CEREBELLUM:

THE STANDARD DEVIANTS™ VIDEO COURSE REVIEW

- Accounting
- Microeconomics
- Statistics
- Biology
- Physics
- Basic Math
- Trigonometry 1 & 2
- Algebra 1 & 2
- Psychology
- Astronomy
- Pre-Calculus 1 & 2
- Calculus 1 & 2
- Chemistry 1, 2, & 3
- Finance 1, 2, & 3
- Organic Chemistry 1, 2, & 3

For an updated list of titles available, check our web site:

www.cerebellum.com

Printed in the beautiful U.S.A.

HOW TO USE THIS BOOK

CHECK OUT THE VIDEOS. Please notice the plural **videos**! This single workbook corresponds to two of our Video Course Reviews: *The Rockin' World of Geology Parts 1 and 2*. You'll be much better off if you buy and watch both tapes.

FOLLOW ALONG. The **VIDEO NOTES** section does your work for you! We've already taken all of your notes—all you have to do is follow along with the videos. We've even given you a **VIDEO TIME CODE** for both videos. Just reset your VCR counter to 0:00:00 when the Cerebellum logo appears at the beginning of each tape. These clocks 0:00:00 give you the time code for each important section so you know where to fast-forward to! This will enable you to learn and retain material much more effectively. Just stop the tape after a difficult section and read through your notes!

Also, so you'll know which video we're talking about, we've put these markers in the upper right-hand corner: **V1** and **V2**. **V1** means you're in a section that covers material from *The Rockin' World of Geology Part 1*. **V2** means you're in a section that covers material from *The Rockin' World of Geology Part 2*.

Study Sidekick

Learn New Stuff. Unfortunately, we just can't include everything about geology in two videos. The **OTHER IMPORTANT STUFF** section gives other cool facts you'll need to ace your tests.

Test Yourself. **QUIZZES** and **PRACTICE EXAMS** allow you to test yourself and make sure you've covered all the bases. The answers appear at the back—*don't cheat!*

Have Fun. The book is chock-full of diversions and stress relievers, and there are two neat flippy pictures at the bottom of each page.

TABLE OF CONTENTS

VIDEO TIME CODES

VIDEO NOTES

TEST YOURSELF

VIDEO NOTES

TABLE OF CONTENTS

STRESS RELIEF

TEST YOURSELF

STUDY SIDEKICK

OTHER IMPORTANT STUFF

ANSWERS

Table of Contents

THE STANDARD DEVIANTS

STUDY SIDEKICK

VIDEO TIME CODE

The Rockin' World of Geology Part 1

0:02:06 **...... I. Principles**

0:02:14 .... A. Geologic Time: The Earth in Context

0:04:25 .... 1. relative dating

0:04:57 .... 2. absolute dating

0:05:04 .... 3. deep time: an overview

0:13:06 .... B. Principles of Geology

0:13:56 .... 1. the geologic record

0:16:37 .... 2. fundamental principles of geology

0:27:59 .... C. Minerals

0:28:57 .... 1. crystalline and amorphous structures

0:33:22 .... 2. physical properties

0:39:54 **...... II. Processes**

0:39:57 .... A. Magma and Intrusive Rocks

0:40:35 .... 1. the difference between lava and magma

0:40:56 .... 2. types of igneous rock

0:43:40 .... 3. plutons

0:45:25 .... 4. igneous textures and colors

0:47:30 .... 5. types of magma

6. magmatic differentiation and Bowen's reaction series	0:50:46
B. Volcanic Rocks and Processes	1:01:10
1. lava	1:01:32
2. pyroclastic materials	1:02:40
3. volcanic edifices	1:04:42
4. locations of volcanoes	1:08:37
C. Weathering and Erosion	1:11:52
1. physical weathering	1:12:07
2. chemical weathering	1:14:54
3. factors that affect weathering	1:17:56
4. erosion	1:19:57
D. Sedimentation and Sedimentary Rocks	1:23:28
1. the rock cycle	1:24:28
2. clastic sedimentary rocks	1:26:16
3. chemical sedimentary rocks	1:29:16
4. biochemical sedimentary rocks	1:31:07
5. paleoenvironments	1:31:27
6. stratification	1:32:30
7. sedimentary facies	1:34:27

VIDEO NOTES

The Rockin' World of Geology Part 1

0:02:06

Principles

0:02:14

Section A: Geologic Time: The Earth in Context

Geologists study the Earth. Like doctors, geologists have specialties. For example, some focus on the oceans, others on the interior of the Earth, and some even study other planets.

The many disciplines of **geology** are separated into two broad categories:

- ▲ **historical geology**
- ▲ **physical geology**

Historical geologists look at the formation and evolution of the Earth, and study life on Earth.

Physical geologists study what materials the Earth is made of, and what's happening on and beneath the Earth's surface. Since most introductory geology classes focus on physical geology, *The Rockin' World of Geology Parts 1 and 2* and this Study Sidekick workbook focus on physical geology, too.

Video Notes

230 million years ago
during the Triassic Period
of the Mesozoic Era

When we talk about the time period before humans were around on Earth, we're talking about a long, long, long time. If the 4.6 billion years of the Earth's history were compacted into one year, the first life-forms would appear in the spring, the **dinosaurs** wouldn't be around until mid-December, and humans wouldn't appear until late in the day on December 31st! Humans have only been around for a fraction of one percent of the Earth's existence. Babies. Mere pups.

By studying the **rocks** on Earth, geologists have constructed a complete record that outlines the geologic time periods in which rocks were formed. There are two types of dating geologists can use to construct time lines:

- ▲ **relative dating**
- ▲ **absolute dating**

0:04:25 **Relative dating** does not assign an age in years to **rock formations** or **geologic events**. Instead, relative dating puts the events in sequential order. The oldest comes first, and subsequent events follow on the relative dating time line.

0:04:57 **Absolute dating** assigns specific dates to rock formation and geologic events. At first, geologists only assigned relative dates to **geologic time** intervals, but advanced dating techniques have allowed them to pinpoint the dates more exactly.

The Geologic Time Scale

The **geologic time scale** is something you just have to memorize. Once you're familiar with the huge scale of geologic time, you can fit events and concepts into that time line, and the big picture of geology will make more sense.

0:05:04 Geologists study **deep time**. Deep time refers to the billions of years that form the Earth's history. We break down huge segments of deep time into **eons, eras, periods,** and **epochs**.

Just as years are divided into months, weeks, and days, the Phanerozoic Eon is divided into eras, periods, and epochs. Think of eras as being roughly like months; periods are shorter, like weeks; and epochs, like days, are even shorter still.

> Gravity is a harsh mistress.
>
> — *The Tick*

WE LIVE IN THE PHANEROZOIC EON, WHICH STARTED 570 MILLION YEARS AGO!

Prior to our Phanerozoic Eon, there were three eons that account for most of the Earth's existence:

- **the Pre-Archean (also known as the Hadean)**
- **the Archean**
- **the Proterozoic**

These three eons are known collectively as the **Pre-Cambrian**. Most of what you'll study has happened during the Phanerozoic Eon—but here's an overview of what came earlier.

The first eon, called the **Pre-Archean (or Hadean)**, began 4.6 billion years ago, at the point in time when scientists believe the Earth formed. Let's translate that number into millions, since we'll measure most time periods in millions of years:

4.6 billion years = 4,600 million years

It's been 4,600 million years since the Earth was formed and the Pre-Archean Eon began. 4,600 million is not quite as much as the number of burgers sold by McDonald's, but that's a lot of years! The Pre-Archean Eon ended 3,800 million years ago.

MORE CRUSTY STUFF:

ROCKS FROM THE PRE-ARCHEAN EON ARE RARE AND HAVE BEEN FOUND ONLY RECENTLY. GEOLOGISTS HAVE HARDLY ANY INFORMATION ABOUT THE FIRST 800 MILLION YEARS OF THE EARTH'S HISTORY!

The Pre-Archean Eon was followed by the **Archean Eon**, which lasted from 3,800 million years ago until 2,500 million years ago. Then came the **Proterozoic Eon**, which lasted from 2,500 million years ago until 570 million years ago, when the Phanerozoic Eon began.

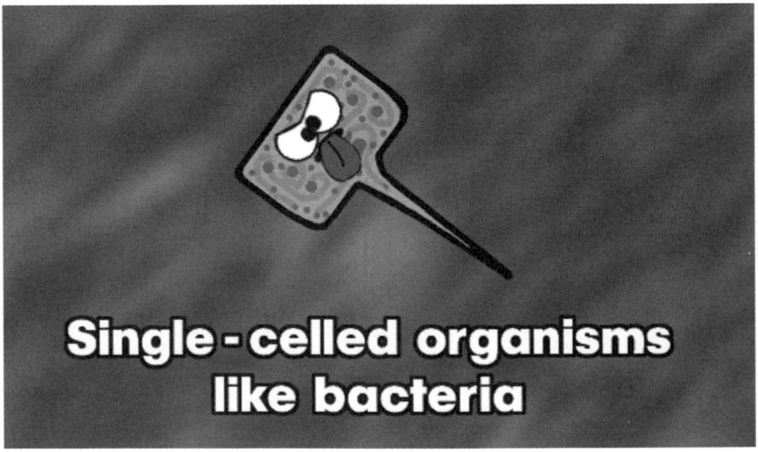

There wasn't much life crawling around in the primordial muck during these eons, but there was some. The earliest **fossils** come from the Archean Eon and date back 3,500 million years. These were single-celled organisms like bacteria—nothing you could hold a conversation with. The first multicellular organisms didn't appear until 700 million years ago during the Proterozoic Eon.

Let's look at the eras and periods (the months and weeks) of the Phanerozoic Eon, because chances are you'll need to be most familiar with these time segments.

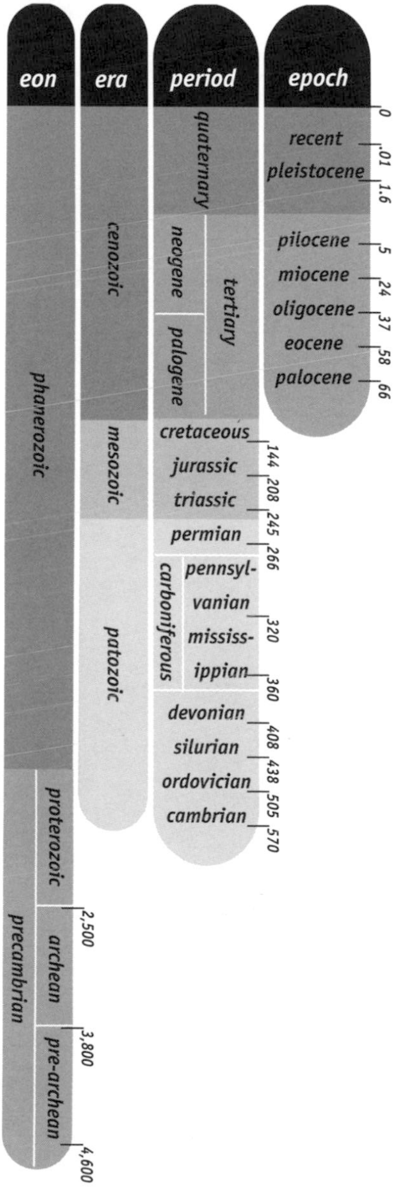

The Phanerozoic Eon is divided into these eras:

- **Paleozoic** (the "old life" era)
- **Mesozoic** (the "middle life" era)
- **Cenozoic** (the "recent life" era)

Complex life-forms existed during all three of these eras.

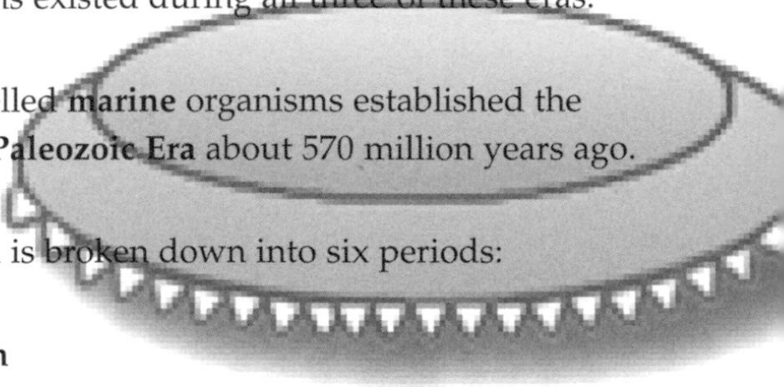

The advent of shelled **marine** organisms established the beginning of the **Paleozoic Era** about 570 million years ago.

The Paleozoic Era is broken down into six periods:

- **Cambrian**
- **Ordovician**
- **Silurian**
- **Devonian**
- **Carboniferous**
  - **(Pennsylvanian)**
  - **(Mississippian)**
- **Permian**

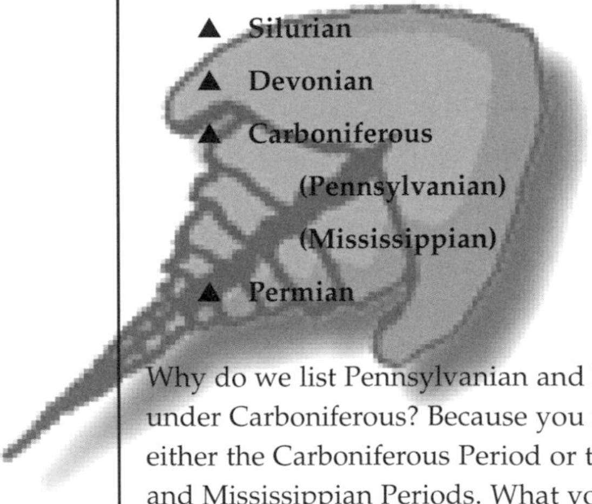

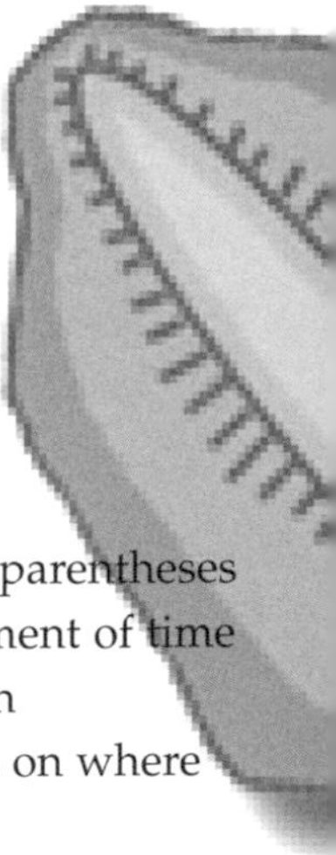

Why do we list Pennsylvanian and Mississippian in parentheses under Carboniferous? Because you can call that segment of time either the Carboniferous Period or the Pennsylvanian and Mississippian Periods. What you call it depends on where you live.

VIDEO NOTES

HERE'S THE DEAL: Periods can be named for their *location* or their *characteristics*.

Location: Geologists distinguish some periods by the area where period's rocks were first studied, or by the geographic location at which the characteristics of that period's rocks are best displayed.

Characteristics: Geologists distinguish other periods by the characteristics of their unique **system** of rocks and **rock formations**. The name **Carboniferous** refers to the period between 360 and 286 million years ago in Europe. Europeans name the period for the characteristics of the rocks (which are rich in carbon or coal) rather than for their geographic location. We name that same period of time differently in the United States. We split it into two periods, and take the names **Pennsylvanian** and **Mississippian** from the predominant geographic locations of the rocks rather than from characteristics of the rocks. The Mississippian Period lasted from 360 until 320 million years ago, and the Pennsylvanian Period lasted from 320 until 286 million years ago.

Life-forms during the Paleozoic Era were quite different from life-forms today. Life on Earth was dominated by fish and sea creatures—some of which were the first animals with shells. The first fish appeared 510 million years ago, toward the end of the **Cambrian** Period of the Paleozoic Era. Land plants didn't start to sprout until 430 million years ago, during the Silurian Period of the Paleozoic Era. There were no animals on land until the end of the Paleozoic Era.

The **Mesozoic Era** is broken down into three periods:

- **Triassic**
- **Jurassic**
- **Cretaceous**

The name **Mesozoic** means "middle life." The Mesozoic is often called "The Age of the Reptiles." Dinosaurs, which are reptiles, were the product of the Earth's mid-life crisis. They raised their little pea-brained heads 230 million years ago, during the **Triassic** Period of the Mesozoic Era. The reptiles were joined by early mammals about 222 million years ago, also during the Triassic Period. Luckily, the dinosaurs became extinct during the **Cretaceous** Period, bringing the Mesozoic Era to an end before humans ever appeared on the scene.

The **Cenozoic Era** was named for "young life" or "recent life," since the animals of the early Cenozoic were very similar to the animals of today. The Cenozoic began 66 million years ago and is often called "The Age of Mammals." It's divided into two periods:

- **Tertiary**
- **Quaternary**

The first horses appeared 53 million years ago, during the early part of the **Tertiary** Period. Humans didn't show up until 4 million years ago, during the latter part of the Tertiary Period. We live in the **Quaternary** Period.

EXTRA MATTER

It's likely your professor will want you to memorize the names of the eras and periods of the Phanerozoic Eon. It's not too hard if you use a mnemonic (memory) device. All you have to do is come up with sentences using the first letter of each period as the first letter of each word in your sentence. Just be sure your word order follows the order of the periods.

Here's an example...

"Paleozoic" starts with "**P**" like "party," so think of Paleozoic as the Partying era. To remember the periods of the Paleozoic Era, you could use this sentence:

"**C**ome **O**ver **S**aturday, **D**ude, **M**y **P**lace is **P**artying."

The word "**C**ome" stands for "**C**ambrian," the first period of the era. "**O**ver" stands for "**O**rdovician," the second period. "**S**aturday" stands for "**S**ilurian," and so on.

So, if you call the Paleozoic Era the partying era, then think of the next era, the Mesozoic, as the messy era--you always have a mess after a party. Use this sentence as your mnemonic for the periods of the Mesozoic Era:

"**T**ry **J**uggling **C**rumbs."

"**T**" stands for "**T**riassic"; "**J**" stands for "**J**urassic"; and "**C**" stands for "**C**retaceous." Juggling crumbs would definitely be messy. Messy--Mesozoic--get it?

Next comes the Cenozoic Era. "**C**enozoic" starts with "**C**" like the word "clean," so now you clean up after the messy party. The periods in the Cenozoic are "**T**ertiary" and "**Q**uaternary," so your mnemonic sentence could be:

"Tidy Quickly."

The Partying Paleozoic said,"Come Over Saturday, Dude, My Place is Partying."

The Messy Mesozoic said,
"Try Juggling Crumbs."

The Clean Cenozoic said,
"Tidy Quickly."

Check out This Other Important Stuff:

1. Detailed time line including details of names and tertiary epochs. See **OTHER IMPORTANT STUFF 1**, page 222.
2. Radiometric dating. See **OTHER IMPORTANT STUFF 2**, page 223.

QUIZ

Quiz 1

1. What are the two types of dating geologists use?

2. What is the age of the Earth? Give your answer in both millions of years and billions of years.

3. Mesozoic means ___________, and is subdivided into the three periods: the ___________, ___________, and ___________.

4. Mammals have been present on Earth since the Proterozoic. True or False?

5. What does a physical geologist study?

6. What life-forms were dominant in the Paleozoic?

Study Sidekick

7. Fill out this geologic time scale.

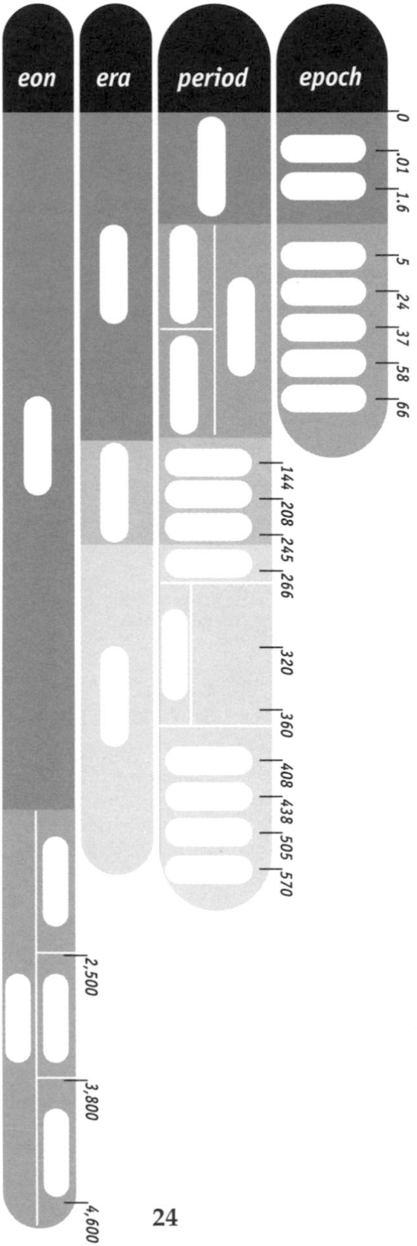

Section B: Principles of Geology

0:13:06

Geologists spend a lot of time studying rocks. Why the heck would they want to do that? Because rocks are like history books. As the Earth has changed over the past 4,600 million years, it has written its story in the rocks. Geologists learn to read rocks like history books.

Most sciences have their own languages, so to speak, so get ready to learn to the language of rock!

0:13:56

Geologists call their hard and lumpy library of rock history books the **geologic record**. The Grand Canyon is like one whole wing of the Library of Congress. There's a vast amount of information and history written into the cliffs and crags of the Grand Canyon, so naturally, geologists have a field day there.

Don't underestimate the importance of gravel.
— Danny Mason the Stonemason

The Canyon's layered **beds** of rock contain information about the Earth and its life-forms from way back before humans were around. For instance, even though the Grand Canyon sits on a plateau 7,500 feet above sea level, there are marine fossils (preserved remains of animals that once lived in the sea) in its rock beds. Pretty freaky, huh? Luckily, we have geologists around to figure out how that happened.

Geologists are "Earth detectives." They collect clues from their observations of the geologic record to figure out what happened in the Earth's past. Detectives solving crimes look for things like fingerprints and bloody gloves to lead them to answers; geologist detectives look for specific clues in the rocks.

Sedimentary rocks give geologists many clues to what was happening on Earth when the rocks were formed, because sedimentary rocks contain stuff that was around at the time of the rocks' formation. Sedimentary rocks are made from **sediments**: things like little pieces of **gravel**, sand, silt, and clay, as well as the remains of animals and plants. Sediment gets carried around and left behind by water, wind, and glaciers.

Most sedimentary rocks come from sediments deposited on the ocean floor, usually within 200 kilometers of the shore. As more and more sediment is deposited on top, older sediment gets buried. This burial results in **compaction** and **cementation**. This overall process is called **lithification**: the process of turning a sediment into a sedimentary rock. Often, plant and animal remains that were present in the sediment are preserved in the sedimentary rock. Scientists get pretty excited when they come across the preserved remains of some wacky prehistoric thing, because the remains are big clues to the Earth's past.

Rocks hold more clues than just the preserved plants and animals. The way rock beds are situated in relation to each other and to the Earth tells a lot about how and when the rocks were formed. There are several **fundamental principles** that Earth detectives use as they gather clues about the geologic history of an area. These clues help them establish the relative ages of sedimentary rocks. **Relative age** refers to the age of rocks in relation to other rocks. Relative age shows the sequence in which a group of rocks formed, and indicates which rock is the oldest, which one formed next, and which is the youngest. It does not assign a numerical age in years. 0:16:37

The following fundamental principles give you a general understanding of how layers of sedimentary rocks were initially deposited. They can help you determine when and where each layer formed. Once you know these general principles, you can apply what you know to the rocks and formations around you, and impress the heck out of your friends.

Let's look at the Grand Canyon in terms of these fundamental principles.

1. The Principle of Original Horizontality

Geologists know that sediments are deposited in horizontal beds. As the sediments settle to the bottom of the ocean and accumulate, they lie in a layer on the horizontal ocean floor. The area that is now the Grand Canyon was once under lots of water, and the sediments that settled out of the water formed the layers we now see on the **canyon** walls. As each layer got buried underneath the next and lithified (formed into rock), the layering was preserved.

The principle of **original horizontality** states that if beds of lithified sediments aren't lying horizontally, then something caused them to move. A sedimentary rock with vertical layering is a clue that something powerful enough to move the rock from its original horizontal position must have occurred. A sedimentary rock that is now vertical must have formed lying flat on the bottom of the ocean, and later got turned up on its side. You have to keep exploring to figure out what moved the rock, but the principle of original horizontality gives us the first

clue to the geologic history of the area where the rock was formed. It takes tremendous power to flip big hunks of rock.

There are a number of powerful phenomena that can move and flip rocks. These processes, like **folding** and **faulting**, are the same ones that help form **mountains**.

2. The Principle of Superposition

If a rock bed hasn't been disturbed since it was formed, you know it is younger than the layer of rock below it. The layers of rock in the Grand Canyon illustrate this principle as well. The canyon's layers of sedimentary rock are piled on top of each other. Each layer looks a little different, so you can see roughly where one layer ends and the next begins. The top layer is the last one to form. This phenomenon is called the principle of **superposition**.

If you want to study the most recent layer of sedimentary rock in an area, study the top layer—that is, unless the rock layers have been disturbed and overturned. If you use absolute dating techniques and find out that a layer of sedimentary rock on top is older than the rocks below it, you have a clue that something disturbed the rock layers and flipped them over.

NOT A DEPOSITIONAL BASIN

3. The Principle of Lateral Continuity

According to this principle, sediments are initially deposited in a layer that extends horizontally in all directions. The layer thins out and ends eventually. The area where the sediments were deposited is called the **depositional basin**.

4. The Principle of Cross-Cutting Relationships

A **cross-cutting relationship** forms when molten rock, called **magma**, pushes its way through an existing bed of sedimentary rock. The magma moves quickly, making its way through existing cracks, forming new cracks, and melting some of the rock it travels through. When the magma cools, the new **igneous** rock cuts across the old sedimentary rock. (An igneous rock is simply a rock formed from cooled and **crystallized** magma. (See Section A of "Processes" for more details on igneous rocks.) When you see a cross-cutting relationship, you know that the rock that was cut through is older than the intruding igneous rock.

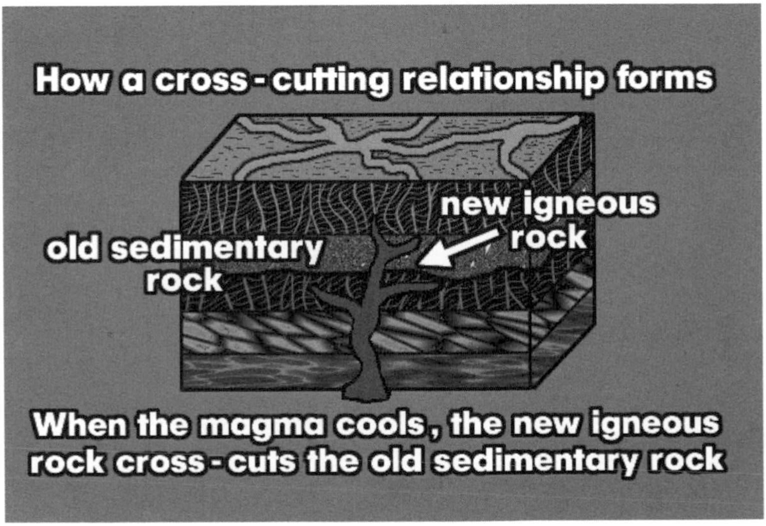
How a cross-cutting relationship forms
new igneous rock
old sedimentary rock
When the magma cools, the new igneous rock cross-cuts the old sedimentary rock

The rock that cuts the bed isn't an original feature of the formation. The rocks on either side of the intruding rock are exactly alike and the intruding igneous rock, which looks different, obviously shoved its way into the original bed. According to the law of cross-cutting relationships, the intruding rock is younger than the rocks it penetrates.

Is this the party to whom I am speaking?

– Lily Tomlin as Ernestine the Operator

5. The Principle of Fossil Succession

The principle of **fossil succession**, which is sometimes called **faunal** and **floral succession**, is a lot like the principle of superposition, but deals specifically with fossils.

We often find fossils in sedimentary rocks. Since life-forms have changed so much over the years, groups of fossils from different time periods are different from one another. The principle of superposition says that if the rocks are undisturbed, the oldest layers of rock should be on the bottom and will have older fossils in them. If we know the age of the rocks, we can figure out the age of the fossils in the rocks. Conversely, if we know the age of the fossils in the rocks, we can figure out the age of the rocks.

6. The Principle of Uniformitarianism

No, **uniformitarianism** is not a religious sect; it only sounds like one. According to the principle of uniformitarianism, you can understand geologic events of the past by observing the geologic events happening right now. By "geologic events," we mean earthquakes and volcanoes and stuff. According to uniformitarianism, we can figure that a volcano eruption now is pretty much like a volcano eruption was a million years ago.

There can, however, be problems with the principle of uniformitarianism. Factors affecting the Earth's processes have changed through time, so we can't really be sure that the processes we see today happen exactly the same way or at exactly the same rate as they did ages ago.

SUMMARY

Geologists use a set of fundamental principles to gather information about the geologic history of the area in which they find certain rocks.

- The principle of original horizontality says that as layers of sediment settle, get buried, and harden into rock, they are oriented horizontally. If a bed of sedimentary rock is not lying horizontally, then something moved it.

- The principle of superposition says that the bottom layer of rock is the oldest in a sedimentary rock sequence. The layers of rock get successively younger as you get closer to the top of the sequence. The top layer of sediment was most recently deposited.

- The principle of **lateral continuity** says that sediments are deposited initially in a layer that extends horizontally in all directions.

- The principle of cross-cutting relationships says that an igneous rock that intrudes into a bed of existing rock is younger than the rock it cuts into.

- The principle of fossil succession, also known as faunal and floral succession, says that the oldest fossils should be in the bottom layers of sedimentary rocks, since those layers of rock are the oldest. If you know how old the rocks are, you should know how old the fossils in the rocks are, and vice-versa.

- The principle of uniformitarianism says that you can understand geologic events of the past by observing the geologic events that are happening right now.

Check out This Other Important Stuff:

For more about the principle of unconformities, see **OTHER IMPORTANT STUFF 3**, page 227.

Quiz 2

1. Why are sedimentary rocks important for us to understand the history of the Earth?

2. Uniformitarianism is often referred to as the principle of "the present is the key to the past." Explain this using an example.

3. What can we assume if we see folded sedimentary beds?

4. What is lithification?

5. Name the 6 fundamental principles that guide geologists as they study sedimentary rocks to collect clues about Earth's history.

6. A geologist is working in California. She sees rocks on the top of a sedimentary rock bed that she knows contain trilobites from the Paleozoic, and rocks on the bottom that contain dinosaurs from the Mesozoic. Explain how this could happen and which fundamental principle she uses.

7. The Grand Canyon was always above sea level. True or False?

QUIZ

8. A geologist is in Virginia, walking on a sedimentary rock. He assumes the rock will continue in all directions from where he is standing. What principle is he using?

9. If we see marine fossils in Ohio, we assume that Ohio was once under ocean water. What principle are we using?

Section C: Minerals

0:27:59 Rocks are made of **minerals**, so to understand rocks, we have to understand minerals. A mineral is an inorganic **solid** found in nature. It has a unique **chemical composition** and **crystal structure**. Does it sound like we're about to talk **chemistry** instead of geology? Yup, we are.

Much of geology is based on chemistry. Here are a few concepts and terms you need to be familiar with to understand minerals and how they come together to form rocks.

IF YOU NEED TO LEARN MORE ABOUT ATOMS AND IONS, VALENCE SHELLS, BONDS, AND ALL THAT STUFF, CHECK OUT *THE SUPER-CHARGED WORLD OF CHEMISTRY PARTS 1, 2, AND 3.*

The chemical make-up and crystal structure of minerals—in other words, the way the **elements** interact and bond—give minerals their characteristic shapes, color, and hardness. Chemical properties of elements and bonds dictate how minerals are formed. The abundance of certain elements in the Earth, along with the chemical properties of those elements, cause certain minerals to be more prevalent than others.

0:28:57 **Crystalline** solids are made up of **atoms** bonded in a three-dimensional geometric pattern. The mineral halite (a.k.a. sodium chloride, NaCl, or plain old table salt), has a crystal structure. Note the three-dimensional geometric structure formed by the bonded atoms.

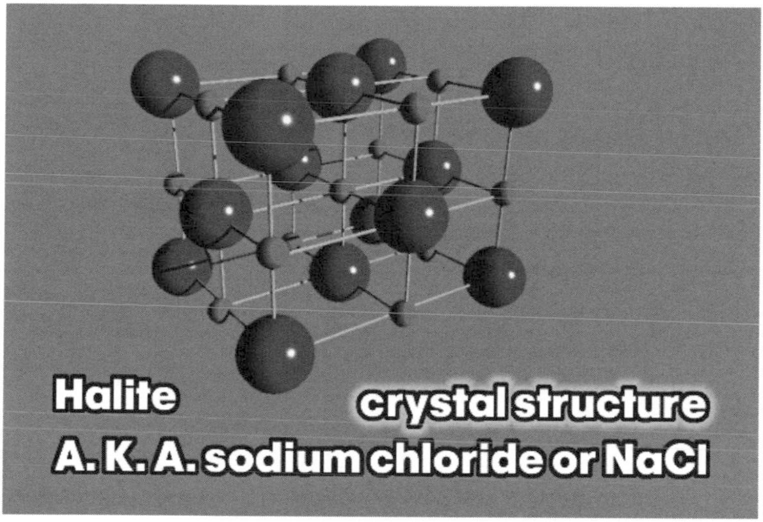

Solids without crystal structures are called **amorphous**, which means "without form." The elements making up amorphous solids don't form geometric structures like the ones in crystalline solids. Naturally occurring **amber** and glass are examples of amorphous solids. Even naturally occurring glass is not a mineral because its atoms don't form a crystal structure.

Sometimes minerals with the same chemical composition can have different crystal structures depending on how the elements bond to each other. For example, diamonds and **graphite** are both made of only carbon. Graphite is plain old pencil lead. You know that diamonds are nothing like pencil lead—if they were, you could give your betrothed an engagement pencil. So how can it be that diamonds and graphite have the exact same chemical composition?

The crystal structure of diamond is quite different from the crystal structure of graphite. It's the way the carbon bonds to itself that makes diamond very hard and graphite very soft. Diamond and graphite are called polymorphs—"poly" meaning "many," and "morphs," meaning "shapes." **Polymorphs** are minerals with the same chemical formula but different crystal structures.

Isomorphs are the opposite of polymorphs. "Iso" means "same" and "morphs" means "shapes," so isomorphs are two minerals that have the same crystal structure but different chemical compositions. **Galena** and halite are examples of isomorphs. Both have a crystal structure that forms a perfect cube, but galena is composed of lead and sulfur, and halite is composed of sodium and chlorine.

galena
halite
galena
is composed of
lead sulfide
halite
is composed of
sodium chloride

The most common elements in the Earth's **crust** are oxygen and silicon. It follows that the most common rock-building minerals are **silicates**, which are minerals containing abundant oxygen and silicon. The silicate ion is made up of one silicon atom surrounded by four oxygen atoms, which forms a **silicate-trahedra** or four-faced pyramid. This is the basic building block of silicate minerals.

Computers in the future may weigh no more than 1.5 tons.

— *Popular Mechanics*, forecasting the relentless march of science, 1949

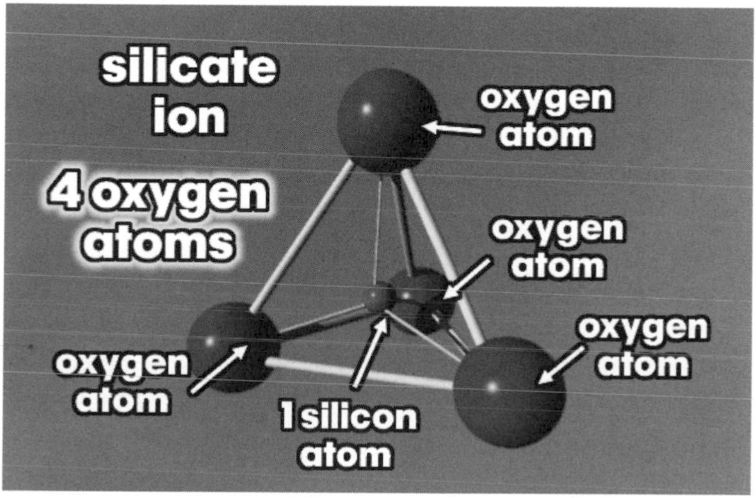

Quartz is a mineral composed entirely of silicon and oxygen. The silica tetrahedra in quartz share every corner oxygen with adjacent silica tetrahedra, binding the silicate ions together in a three-dimensional network. Quartz's tight bonding pattern makes it very hard and difficult to break.

In some minerals, the silica tetrahedra are not as tightly bound to one another, and the result is a mineral that is soft and easy to break. For example, minerals called **micas** are composed of two-dimensional sheets of silica tetrahedra. Because the sheets are not tightly bound to one another, the sheets pull apart readily like pages of a book.

I think there is a world market for maybe five computers.

— Thomas Watson, chairman of IBM, 1943

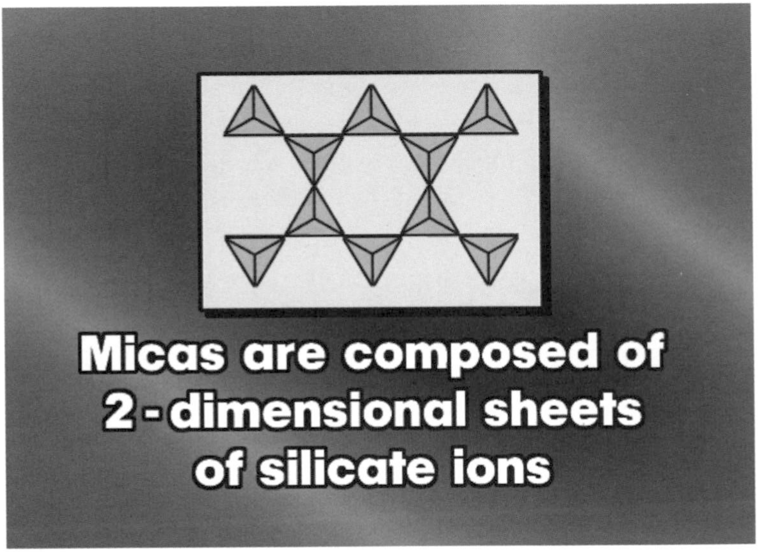

Micas are composed of 2-dimensional sheets of silicate ions

0:33:22

The **physical properties** of minerals are dictated by their chemical composition and crystal structure. Minerals are identified and classified by their measurable physical properties:

- **hardness**
- **cleavage**
- **fracture**
- **luster**
- **color**

AN EXTRA SHOVEL-FULL

Check it out—you'll probably see this stuff on your test!

Hardness

A mineral's **hardness** is its ability to resist abrasion. A guy named Friedrich Mohs devised a hardness scale we use to measure and compare the hardness of minerals. The Mohs hardness scale rates 10 minerals: from diamond, the hardest mineral, to **talc**, a very soft mineral.

Mohs Hardness Scale

Hardness	*Mineral*
10	Diamond
9	Corundum
8	Topaz
7	Quartz
6	Orthoclase
5	Apatite
4	Fluorite
3	Calcite
2	Gypsum
1	Talc

Quartz will scratch **calcite** because it is harder than calcite; but calcite won't scratch quartz. Calcite will scratch gypsum, because gypsum is softer than calcite. Other minerals are tested for their hardness relative to the minerals on the scale.

Cleavage

Cleavage is the way that crystalline minerals split or break along planar surfaces. Where and how minerals split, or cleave, depends on the strength and arrangement of the bonds in their crystal structure.

Fracture

Fracture is a lot like cleavage, but a fracture is a break along an uneven surface rather than along a planar surface. Any mineral will fracture if enough pressure is applied to it.

Luster

Luster refers to the way that minerals reflect light. There are two types of luster:

- **Metallic**: The mineral looks like a metal when light reflects off it. Galena, for example, is composed of lead and sulfur and has a metallic luster.
- **Nonmetallic**: The mineral may look glassy, greasy, waxy, brilliant, dull, or earthy.

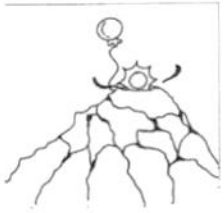

Color

Minerals of the same type will frequently be the same color, but this is not always the case. For example, **fluorite** can be purple, green, blue, or yellow; but many minerals, such as **pyrite**, never vary in color. Pyrite is always brassy, as any fool knows, but only gold is golden.

STUDY SIDEKICK

SUMMARY

- A mineral is an inorganic crystalline solid found in nature. It has a unique chemical composition and crystal structure.

- Solid materials that lack crystal structures are called amorphous solids.

- Polymorphs are minerals that have the same chemical formula, but different crystal structures (such as diamond and graphite).

- An isomorph is the opposite of a polymorph. Isomorphs are minerals that have the same crystal structure but different chemical compositions (such as galena and halite).

- We describe minerals in terms of their measurable physical properties.

    1. Hardness: the ability to resist abrasion.

    2. Cleavage: the way that crystalline minerals split or break along planar surfaces.

    3. Fracture: the way minerals break along uneven surfaces.

4. Luster: the way minerals reflect light (metallic or nonmetallic).

5. Color: specimens of the same mineral are often (but not always) different colors.

Eating an artichoke is like getting to know someone really well.

– Willi Hastings

Check out This Other Important Stuff:

1. Silicate mineral structure. See **OTHER IMPORTANT STUFF 4**, page 231.

2. Other physical properties. See **OTHER IMPORTANT STUFF 5**, page 232.

3. Main rock-forming minerals. See **OTHER IMPORTANT STUFF 6**, page 233.

Quiz 3

1. What is a mineral?

2. Is amber (fossilized tree resin) a mineral? Why?

3. Explain how you use the Mohs scale of hardness.

4. Is color useful for identifying a mineral?

5. What is a crystalline solid?

6. What is a polymorph? Give an example.

7. Name and briefly describe the 5 main physical properties that are used to identify minerals.

8. A silicate mineral always contains the two elements __________ and __________.

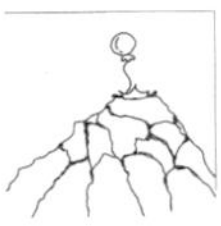

Processes 0:39:54

Section A: Magma and Intrusive Rocks 0:39:57

Magma is molten rock below the Earth's surface. It's a **siliceous** (silica-rich) liquid with a chemical composition like that of the Earth's crust. As a matter of fact, magma is just liquid Earth-crust.

Lava is magma that has made it up through the Earth's crust to the surface. Once the magma shoots out of a **volcano** or oozes out of a crack of some sort, it's called lava. 0:40:35

Rocks that form from cooling magma or lava are called **igneous rocks**. "Igneous" is a general term that describes rocks that form from magma or the accumulation of the stuff that oozes or shoots out of a volcano (like lava and ash).

There are two broad categories of igneous rock:

- ▲ **extrusive igneous rock**
- ▲ **intrusive igneous rock**

Extrusive igneous rock forms from lava, so it cools and crystallizes on the Earth's surface. Extrusive igneous rock is also called **volcanic igneous rock**. 0:40:56

"EXTRUSIVE" COMES FROM THE WORD "EXTRUDE," WHICH MEANS "TO FORCE OR PUSH OUT." REMEMBER "EX" MEANS "OUT." EXTRUSIVE IGNEOUS ROCK HAS *EXITED* THE SURFACE OF THE EARTH.

Tuff is an extrusive igneous rock.

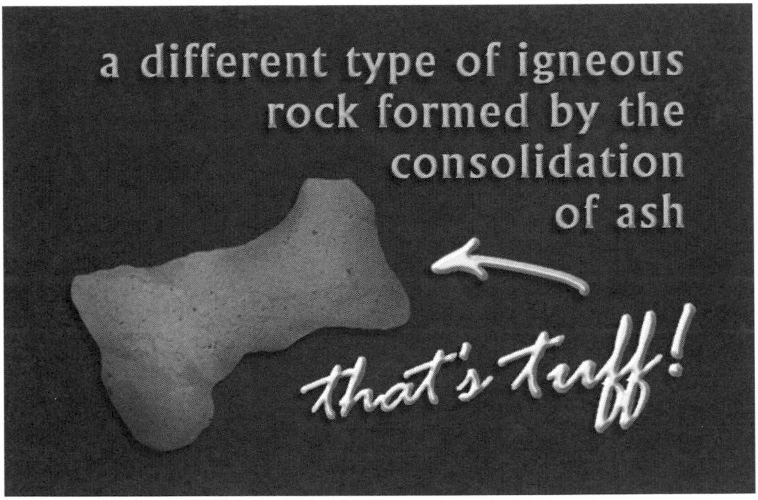
a different type of igneous rock formed by the consolidation of ash
that's tuff!

Sometimes magma doesn't make it out of the crust, but cools and forms solid rock anyway. Magma that cools and crystallizes within the Earth's crust is called **intrusive igneous rock.** Intrusive igneous rock is also called **plutonic igneous rock**.

THE WORD "INTRUSIVE" WILL REMIND YOU THAT THESE ROCKS FORMED FROM MAGMA THAT COOLED *INSIDE* THE EARTH'S CRUST.

0:42:40

Magma cools beneath the Earth's surface, and the lump of solid igneous rock that forms is called a **pluton**.

Video Notes

There are two kinds of plutons:

- **concordant plutons**
- **discordant plutons**

Concordant plutons lie parallel to the layers of rock that were already there when the pluton formed. The pre-existing rock is often called the **country rock**. Concordant plutons lie parallel to the country rock.

WHEN YOU THINK OF "CONCORDANT," THINK OF THE CONCORDE AIRPLANE THAT FLIES PARALLEL TO THE GROUND.

Some days I'm a dynamo and others I'm just a mo.

— Kristie W., Senior Cerebellum writer

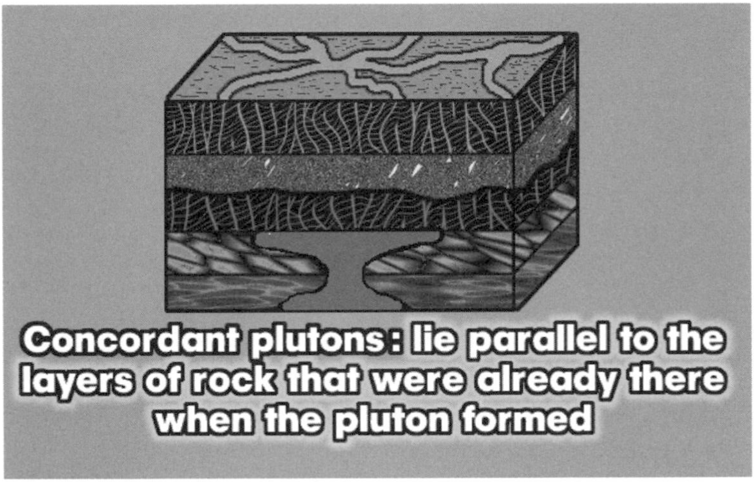
Concordant plutons: lie parallel to the layers of rock that were already there when the pluton formed

Discordant plutons cut across the layers of existing country rock. "Dis" is a prefix that means "to do the opposite of." Discordant plutons diss the country rock—they do their own thing and go their own way.

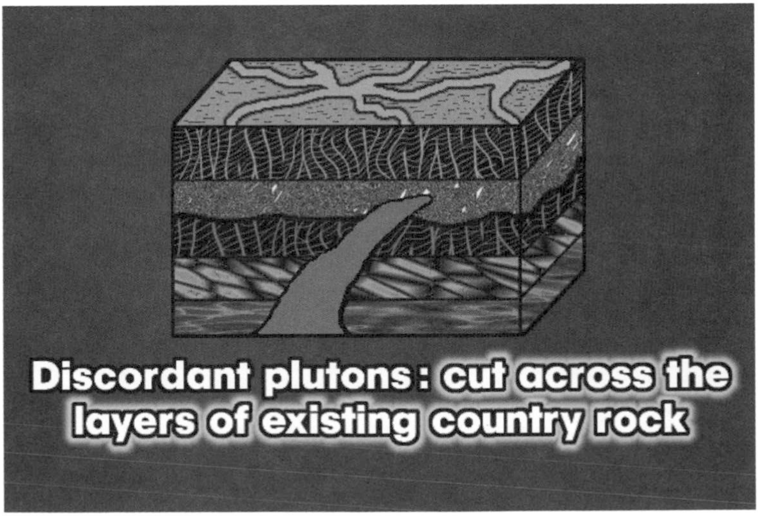
Discordant plutons: cut across the layers of existing country rock

Even though plutons form beneath the surface of the Earth, the beds of country rock around and overlying the pluton may **erode** to expose the pluton and the bed of rock it cuts through. Look for more about erosion and **weathering** later on in Section C.

There are several categories of plutons:

- **batholiths**
- **stocks**
- **dikes**
- **sills**

The largest plutons are called **batholiths**. By definition, batholiths must be at least 100 square kilometers in area. That's 38 square miles! Think of it: a giant igneous rock that covers 38 or more square miles. You could build a city on a batholith.

Discordant plutons smaller than 100 square kilometers are called **stocks**. Many plutons called "stocks," however, are actually just the exposed part of much larger plutons.

Dikes and **sills** are both plutons that form in broad, thin sheets. The difference between dikes and sills is that dikes are discordant, so they cut across the layers of country rock.

DISCORDANT DIKES--BOTH START WITH D!

Sills are concordant, so they lie parallel to the country rock.

SILL SOUNDS LIKE WINDOWSILL, AND WINDOWSILLS ARE PARALLEL TO THE FLOOR. ASSOCIATE SILL WITH WINDOWSILL, AND YOU WILL REMEMBER THAT SILLS ARE CONCORDANT, OR PARALLEL.

0:45:25

The **texture** of an igneous rock will give you a clue about the environment in which the rock formed. For example, the amount of time it takes the magma to cool and crystallize into rock affects the rock's texture. When magma *cools slowly,* it allows more time for crystals to form, so you end up with a coarse-grained rock that has larger crystals.

When magma is **quenched** *quickly,* and the crystals don't have a lot of time to grow, you get a fine-grained rock with small crystals. Sometimes lava flowing from a volcano cools so quickly that there's no time for crystals to form at all. When this happens, a volcanic glass like **obsidian** forms.

Sometimes magma starts cooling below the Earth's surface, then it gets forced through the crust and finishes cooling above the ground. A rock that starts forming beneath the surface and finishes forming on the surface is called a **porphyry**. Porphyries have what's called **porphyritic texture**. Porphyritic texture is characterized by larger crystals, called **phenocrysts**, surrounded by a fine-grained matrix of little crystals that form after the magma starts cooling quickly on the surface.

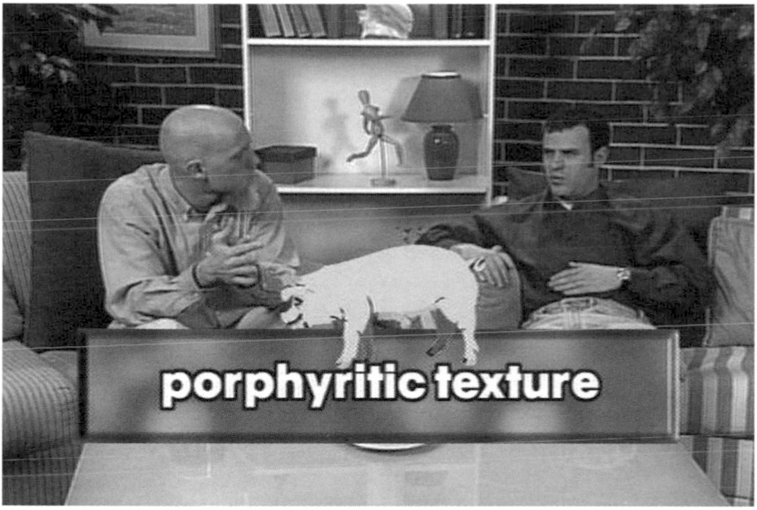

Not all magma is composed of the same stuff, so not all igneous rocks are the same. Magmas are divided into four categories based on their chemical composition: 0:47:30

- **felsic**
- **intermediate**
- **mafic**
- **ultramafic**

Each type of magma yields a different type of igneous rock.

Felsic magma is rich in silica. Silica is a compound made up of oxygen and silicon atoms. Besides silica, felsic magma also contains a considerable amount of sodium, potassium, and aluminum. Felsic magma cools to form igneous rocks such as **granite**.

Magma poorer in silica is called **mafic magma**. Mafic magma forms an igneous rock rich in minerals such as iron and magnesium. Mafic silicate minerals composed largely of iron and magnesium are called **ferromagnesian minerals**. Pyroxene and amphibole are ferromagnesian minerals.

HERE'S A GOOD WAY TO REMEMBER THAT MAFIC MINERALS ARE RICH IN IRON AND MAGNESIUM. THE WORD *MAFIC* CONTAINS AN "M" AND AN "F." *MAGNESIUM* STARTS WITH "M," AND THE CHEMICAL SYMBOL FOR IRON IS "FE."

Intermediate magma has a mineral composition richer in silica than mafic magma, and poorer in silica than felsic magma.

Finally, **ultramafic magma** is even poorer in silica and richer in magnesium and iron than mafic magma.

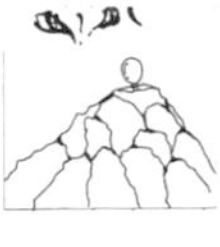

The color of rocks and minerals generally reflects their chemical composition. **Felsic minerals** tend to be light, while mafic and ultramafic minerals tend to be dark. Granite, which is felsic in composition, is a light-colored rock. **Basalt** is mafic, and it has the characteristic dark color of a mafic rock.

Dear Sweetheart:

Last night I thought of you. At least I think it was you.

– Love letter by Snoopy

As magma cools, the uncoordinated ions within it organize themselves into minerals. You can get many different kinds of minerals from magma, because magma contains various mineral-forming elements.

The different types of minerals that form from magma do so in a specific sequence according to each mineral's **freezing temperature** (their **crystallization temperature**, or just the temperature at which a liquid becomes a solid). Some minerals become solid when they're still pretty warm (about 1000°C), and others have to get quite a bit cooler (about 600°C) before they solidify. That's why we say they solidify in a specific sequence. Minerals with higher crystallization temperatures solidify out of the magma first, and minerals that need a lower temperature to solidify form later.

0:50:46

Magma can form igneous rocks with a range of chemical compositions. But here's the crazy thing: All these types of igneous rocks and minerals can form from a *single mafic magma*. When these different rock types come out of one type of magma, it's called **magmatic differentiation**.

Both felsic and mafic magma are liquids composed largely of the elements oxygen, silicon, and aluminum; and each type contains sodium, potassium, and calcium as well. Each type also has at least some magnesium and iron.

- ▲ Mafic magma, in comparison to felsic magma, has a lot more magnesium and iron and a lot less aluminum, potassium, and sodium. It can form a *small quantity* of the silicate minerals that contain aluminum, potassium, and sodium.

▲ Ultramafic magma has more magnesium and iron and less aluminum, potassium, and sodium than mafic magma. It will form an *even smaller quantity* of the silicate minerals that contain aluminum, potassium, and sodium, because it has even less of the necessary elements.

▲ Felsic magma, in comparison to mafic magma, has less magnesium and iron and a lot more aluminum, potassium, and sodium. It can form a *larger quantity* of silicate minerals containing aluminum, potassium, and sodium than mafic magma, because it contains more of the necessary elements.

▲ Intermediate magma is, well, intermediate. It is made up of proportions of elements somewhere between the compositions of felsic and mafic: it contains more magnesium and iron than mafic magma, and less aluminum, potassium, and sodium than felsic magma.

In short, felsic and mafic magma are composed of pretty much the same elements but in different proportions. Both magmas can form some quantity of the various minerals. How much of each type of mineral the magma forms depends on how much of the necessary elements the particular magma contains.

In 1928, N.L. Bowen came up with a theory to explain magmatic differentiation. Based on his observations and experiments, Bowen proposed a general scheme that explains how felsic minerals crystallize from a mafic magma. His scheme is called **Bowen's reaction series**.

One hundred thousand lemmings can't be wrong.

- Graffito

Here are the nuts and bolts of Bowen's theory: As magma cools, not all types of minerals crystallize simultaneously. The minerals with higher freezing temperatures crystallize first, and then other minerals crystallize at successively lower temperatures.

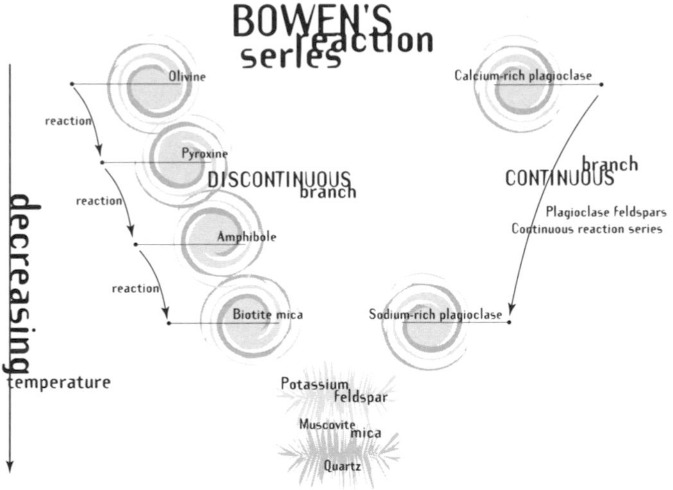

Bowen's reaction series explains the formation of both the felsic and the mafic minerals formed from the magma. The series traces two "branches," or paths, of crystallization that occur during magmatic differentiation:

- A **discontinuous branch**, which accounts for the mafic minerals formed from the magma.

- A **continuous branch**, which accounts for the feldspar minerals produced from the magma.

As the magma cools, crystallization happens at the same time along both paths.

The discontinuous branch accounts for the mafic minerals that form from the magma: the ones called "ferromagnesian" that contain iron and magnesium.

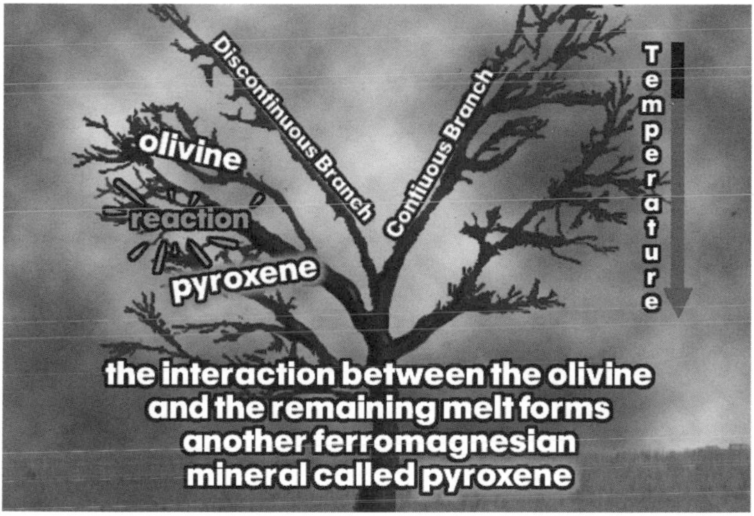
Discontinuous Branch
Contiuous Branch
Temperature
olivine
reaction
pyroxene
the interaction between the olivine and the remaining melt forms another ferromagnesian mineral called pyroxene

As the magma cools, a ferromagnesian mineral called **olivine** starts to crystallize first, because it has the highest freezing temperature of the forming mafic minerals. In other words, olivine solidifies at a relatively high temperature. So now there's some crystallized olivine in the partially cooled magma. Why is olivine a mafic mineral? Because it contains lots of iron and magnesium.

STUDY SIDEKICK

As olivine crystallizes, it uses iron and magnesium and just a little silica out of the **melt**. As the magma continues to cool, the olivine stops forming. The solidified olivine reacts with the remaining melt, which is richer in silica. The interaction between the olivine and the remaining melt forms another ferromagnesian mineral called **pyroxene**. Pyroxene is still rich in iron and magnesium, but has more silica in its crystal structure than olivine. Some of the olivine turns into pyroxene as the reaction occurs, but often the reaction destroying the olivine is incomplete, so you end up with some olivine encased in pyroxene in the cooling magma.

THE PYROXENE ENCASING THE OLIVINE IS CALLED A REACTION RIM.

As the temperature of the magma continues to decrease, the pyroxene reacts with the melt and the **amphibole**, the next ferromagnesian mineral in the series, begins to form. This mineral is again rich in iron and magnesium, but it has more silica than olivine or pyroxene. Then the temperature goes down again, and the amphibole reacts with the melt to form **biotite mica**—and that's the end of the discontinuous branch.

All the minerals formed by the discontinuous branch are mafic, meaning they are rich in iron and magnesium and don't have a tremendous amount of silica and alumina. Note that in the discontinuous branch, a different mineral is produced at each stage in the series.

The continuous branch of Bowen's reaction series uses up some of the elements in the melt that the minerals formed in the discontinuous branch don't use. Remember, the minerals of the continuous branch of the series crystallize *at the same time* as those in the discontinuous branch.

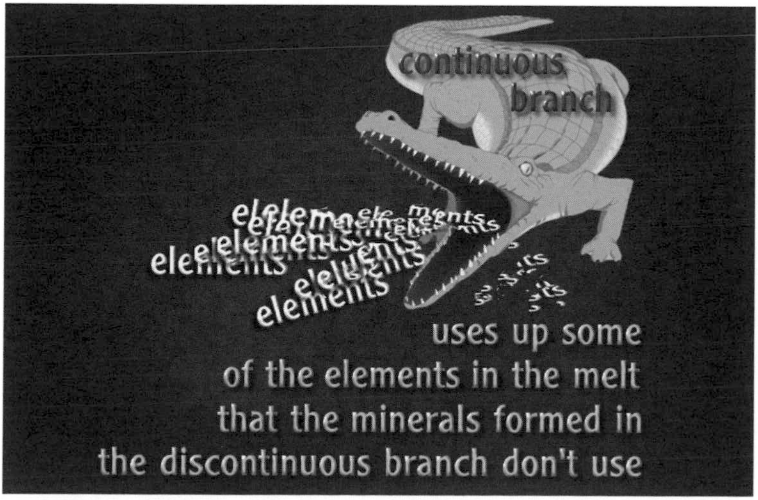

In the continuous branch, all the minerals that form are versions of one type of mineral called **plagioclase feldspar**—that's why the continuous branch is called "continuous." Unlike the discontinuous branch, which produces several different minerals, the continuous branch produces a type of plagioclase feldspar at every step.

WHAT THE HECK IS FELDSPAR?

Feldspars are minerals that, as a group, are the most common mineral type in the Earth's crust. Plagioclase is one of the feldspar minerals. It contains calcium and sodium, two elements that are not used up in the discontinuous branch.

When the magma first starts cooling, it forms a plagioclase that contains a relatively large amount of calcium. The calcium-to-sodium ratio in the early-formed plagioclase is considerably higher than the calcium-to-sodium ratio in the remaining melt. As the melt continues to cool, however, the early-formed, calcium-rich plagioclase reacts with the relatively more sodium-rich melt, and the calcium-rich plagioclase evolves toward a more sodium-rich composition itself. In other words, the early-formed plagioclase changes its composition as the magma cools, so that it contains more sodium. The plagioclase changes as it cools until its calcium-to-sodium ratio is the same as the calcium-to-sodium ratio of the original melt.

Sometimes the early-formed, calcium-rich plagioclase manages to get separated from the melt, causing it to stop reacting and changing. The early plagioclase may sink into a sludge at the bottom of the magma chamber, so it's no longer in contact with

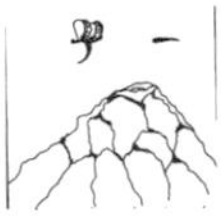

MORE CRUSTY STUFF:

- ▲ **AT EVERY STEP IN THE CONTINUOUS BRANCH, THE MAGMA FORMS PLAGIOCLASE, WHICH IS ONE OF A GROUP OF MINERALS CALLED FELDSPARS.**

- ▲ **AT THE BEGINNING OF THE PROCESS, THE PLAGIOCLASE HAS A HIGHER PROPORTION OF CALCIUM THAN THE MELT, BUT AS THE MELT CONTINUES TO COOL, THE PLAGIOCLASE CHANGES ITS COMPOSITION UNTIL IT HAS THE SAME CALCIUM-TO-SODIUM RATIO AS THE ORIGINAL MELT.**

the melt (this is called **crystal settling**), or the early plagioclase may stop reacting because the rest of the melt migrates to another location in the Earth's crust.

After the continuous and discontinuous branches of the series have run their course, there may still be some melt left over. After the ferromagnesian minerals and plagioclase feldspars have formed, the remainder of the melt is rich in potassium, aluminum, and silicon.

These remaining elements come together to form **potassium feldspar**, another member of the feldspar family cousin to plagioclase feldspar. Then, if the magma is cooling in an area of high water pressure, **muscovite mica** forms. If there's any magma left at this point, it's mostly composed of silicon and oxygen, so the remaining magma cools to form quartz.

Who ever thought cooling could be so complex and interesting?

Check out This Other Important Stuff:

For more about magma and plutons, see **OTHER IMPORTANT STUFF 7**, page 235.

Quiz 4

"Hello," he lied.

– Don Carpenter quoting a Hollywood agent

1. Describe the difference between concordant and discordant plutons.

2. A geologist in the field is mapping a fine-grained igneous rock. She calls it plutonic. Is she right? Explain.

3. What are the four categories of magma?

4. What is the difference between magma and lava?

5. A batholith is a small plutonic rock about the size of a bathtub. True or False?

6. Ultramafic magma has no silicon or oxygen to form silicate minerals. True or False? Explain why or why not.

7. A geologist in the field is mapping a fine-grained igneous rock. If he calls it a volcanic lava flow, is he right? Explain.

8. Explain the difference between the continuous and discontinuous branches of Bowen's reaction series.

9. What is magmatic differentiation?

10. Complete Bowen's reaction series.

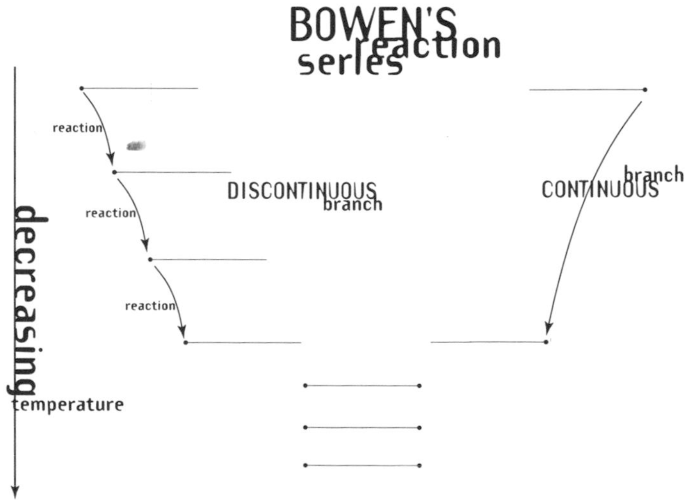

Section B: Volcanic Rocks and Processes

1:01:10

1:01:32

Extrusive igneous rocks are made from the lava and solid material that oozes or shoots out of volcanoes. Here are some terms associated with volcanoes and their processes.

Pahoehoe and **aa** describe two different categories of mafic lava flows.

Pahoehoe flows get their name from the Hawaiian word for "ropy," because this type of flow has a ropy-looking surface. (You know, like a bunch of ropes.) Pahoehoe forms when congealed surface lava is dragged along over hot, moving lava. The congealed part rolls over the hot part, forming folds that look like ropes or sausages.

An **aa** flow has a rough and jagged texture, because it is more thick and viscous than a pahoehoe flow. When it cools, the rock it forms can be sharp and treacherous—so "Ah-ah!" is the sound you'd make if you tried to walk barefoot across it.

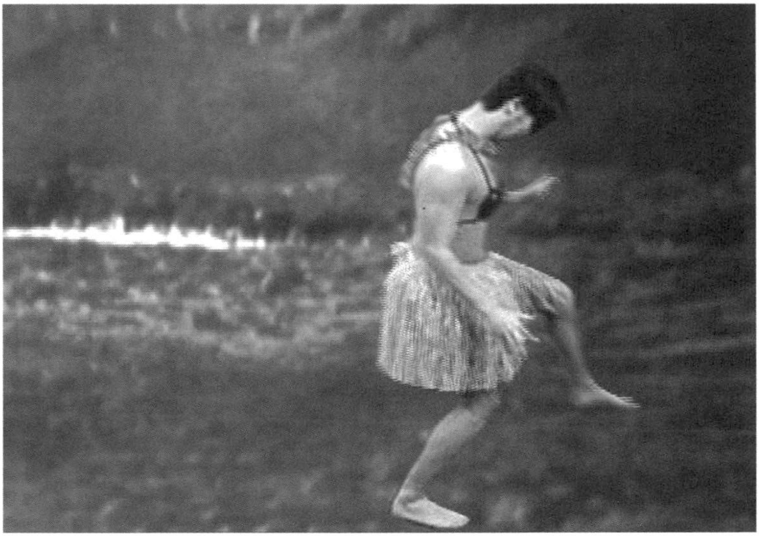

1:02:40

When a volcano erupts, a bunch of junk spews out of it and hardens into what we call **pyroclastic materials**. Pyroclastic materials include:

- **ash**
- **pumice**
- **tuff**

Ash is defined more by its size than by its composition. Ash is anything that shoots out of a volcano and is 2 millimeters or less in diameter. It's the little stuff—this is easy to remember because we generally think of ash as being fine in texture.

pumice
filled with holes that form when gases escape from the lava

Pumice is the rock you use to file the calluses on your feet; but that's not important right now. Pumice is a volcanic glass filled with holes that form when gases escape from the lava. Some pumice forms as a hardened crust on a lava flow, and other times pumice is ejected directly from an explosive eruption.

Tuff is a type of igneous rock formed by the consolidation of ash. Remember, igneous rocks form from cooled lava or magma, or from ash and pyroclastic materials that are spewed out of volcanoes. Sometimes the ash is so hot that when it shoots out of the volcano, it fuses into rock as soon as it comes together. When that happens, the tuff is called **welded tuff**. Welded tuff is more compact and has less open pore space than tuff. In fact, the grains of welded tuff are welded together to the point that it may look like glass.

1:04:42

A **volcanic edifice** is the physical structure of the volcano: its shape and how it's formed. The shape of a volcano is determined by the type and consistency of the magma forced out of it. There are three types of volcanic edifices:

- **shield volcanoes**
- **composite volcanoes (stratovolcanoes)**
- **cinder cones**

Mafic lava, also called **basaltic lava**, isn't very thick or viscous. When runny mafic (basaltic) lava comes out of a volcano, it spreads out in thin layers, producing a broad volcanic edifice called a **shield volcano**.

REMEMBER, MAFIC LAVA HAS LESS SILICA THAN FELSIC LAVA. SILICA (A COMPOUND COMPOSED OF OXYGEN AND SILICON) MAKES LAVA THICK AND VISCOUS. LESS SILICA MEANS THINNER, RUNNIER LAVA.

Shield volcanoes are low and rounded, like a shield lying on the ground with the convex side facing up. Shield volcano eruptions aren't usually terribly explosive, so they aren't as dangerous as other types of volcanoes. That's lucky for Hawaiians, because the Hawaiian volcanoes are shield volcanoes.

Intermediate lava is thicker and more viscous than mafic lava because it contains more silica, which makes it more thick and sticky. Intermediate lava forms some pretty distinctive landscape features.

I have a rock garden. Last week three of them died.

– Richard Diran

The big, concave-sided, symmetrical edifices we typically associate with volcanoes are called **composite volcanoes** or **stratovolcanoes**. These monsters generally erupt thick, intermediate lava with explosive force. Mount St. Helens in Washington state is a composite volcano.

The insides of composite or stratovolcanoes are layered with lava and pyroclastic material. Pyroclastic material is stuff like ash, blocks of pumice, and little bits of volcanic glass—in other words, hardened bits of all the junk that spews out of volcanoes. The pyroclastic material hardens and builds up inside the volcano, alternating with layers of lava. When the volcano erupts, lava flows down the sides and pyroclastic materials come flying out.

Cinder cones are volcanic edifices produced by the buildup of pyroclastic materials. Ash and little hot stuff that looks like cinders shoot out of a vent (an opening in the ground), then fall back down around the vent, forming a steep-sided cone. These cones can grow pretty fast during an eruption, but they rarely get more than 400 meters high. You can often find cinder cones on the sides of bigger volcanoes, like composite volcanoes, where smaller vents on the volcano's flanks spew lava and create a buildup of pyroclasts around the vent.

Fissure eruptions ooze lava so runny that it never forms a volcanic edifice. This runny, mafic, silica-poor lava spreads out into **basalt plateaus**, which are broad areas covered with hardened mafic lava. The Columbia River Plateau and the Snake River Plain in the northwest U.S., all of east Africa, much of northern India, nearly all of the ocean floor, and most of the island of Iceland are composed of huge basalt lava flows that erupted from fissures in the ground or under the sea.

An eruption of hot ash, dust fragments, and hot gases that proceeds downhill with great speed and devastating effects is called a **nuée ardente**. If you see one of these coming, run! In 1902, Mt. Pelée in Martinique erupted, producing a nuée ardente. The cloud of gas and debris that exploded out of the volcano traveled about 100 miles per hour and wreaked tremendous havoc. The layman's word for this phenomenon is "disaster."

In the U.S., we have the Hawaiian volcanoes and a few in the Pacific Northwest. But why aren't there any volcanoes in Washington, D.C.?

VIDEO NOTES

To understand why there's a lot of hot air but no volcanoes in Washington, D.C., we have to understand the basic idea of plate tectonics.

The theory of **plate tectonics** states that the outer part of the Earth is divided up into big **plates** that move around. The two outermost layers of the Earth, the crust and part of the upper mantle, are collectively called the **lithosphere**. Beneath the lithosphere is the **asthenosphere**, which is a hot, partially molten layer.

The lithosphere is divided into a series of continent- or ocean-size plates that can move towards each other, away from each other, or slide past each other, moving on the asthenosphere. When these plates move, they can cause volcanoes, **earthquakes**, and they can even push up mountain ranges...So stay out of the way.

Most of the Earth's volcanoes are at or near the plate boundaries, since the moving plates allow some magma to escape from deeper in the Earth. 1:08:37

- ▲ About 80% of all volcanoes occur at boundaries where the plates *come together.*
- ▲ 15% occur at boundaries where plates *separate* from each other.
- ▲ Only the remaining 5% occur *within* the plates.
- ▲ There aren't any plate boundaries in Washington, DC!

I'm a Mog. Half man, half dog. I'm my own best friend.

– John Candy in *Spaceballs*

There are two major volcano belts in the world. The **Ring of Fire** surrounding the Pacific Ocean contains 60% of all active volcanoes. Another 20% are in the Mediterranean belt, and most of the rest are located on **mid-oceanic ridges** like the **Mid-Atlantic Ridge** which, as its name implies, runs right down the center of the Atlantic Ocean.

AN EXTRA SHOVEL-FULL

Geologists have some luck predicting volcanic eruptions, but there's not much chance that humans will ever be able to control volcanoes. Here's our advice: If you see a volcano erupting, run. Because not only do volcanoes spew hot lava and fast-moving pyroclastic flows everywhere, they also muck up the atmosphere with dust and noxious gases. All the dust they cough up blocks sunlight and can actually reduce the temperature here on Earth.

Quiz 5

1. You are going to be a tour guide in Hawaii. Describe the shape of the volcanoes you will see, the rock type present, and whether an eruption would be explosive.

2. What is the lithosphere?

3. What is the asthenosphere?

4. Name two areas where you can see an active volcano.

5. Are the continental plates found in the lithosphere or asthenosphere?

6. Washington State has volcanoes that are active. They are at the (edge/center) of a continental plate.

7. A student sees a volcano. Remembering his geology class, he calls it a cinder cone. His friend from class says it is a composite volcano. The volcano is 1000 meters high. What is the correct answer?

8. What is a fissure eruption and what type of magma is involved?

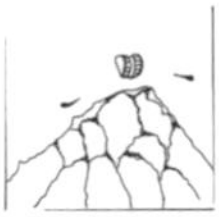

Section C: Weathering and Erosion

1:11:52

Weathering is the disintegration and chemical alteration of the rocks on the Earth's surface.

- Physical weathering, also called mechanical weathering, is the physical breaking of rocks into smaller pieces.
- Chemical weathering is the chemical reaction of rocks with their surroundings.

These two components of weathering occur simultaneously.

1:12:07

Physical (mechanical) weathering breaks rocks up into smaller pieces. There are several processes that work to break rocks up:

- **frost wedging**
- **exfoliation**
- **thermal expansion and contraction**

Frost wedging occurs when rock cracks fill with water. The water freezes and expands, prying the rock apart. Frost wedging is responsible for potholes on roads: When water gets into a small crack in the road, it widens the crack by freezing and thawing a few times.

You are duller than a great thaw.

— *Much Ado About Nothing*

FROST WEDGING
occurs when
rock cracks
fill with
water

Exfoliation occurs when rounded sheets of rock peel off rocks or outcrops.

EXFOLIATION
DOME

An outcrop is the part of a rock formation that sticks out of the ground.

Exfoliation is a lot like layers falling off a big onion. It happens to rocks with sheet joints, which are fractures that run more or less parallel to the surface of the rock. When these fractures break, you get exfoliation. Rounded, sheetlike pieces fall off, producing a rounded blob of rock called an **exfoliation dome**.

Thermal expansion and **contraction** are kinds of weathering attributed to the daily cycle of temperature change.

- When the temperature goes up, rock expands.
- When the temperature goes down, rock contracts.

In most places, this expansion and contraction happens on a small scale every day. In the **desert**, however, the temperature may fluctuate as much as 100°F during the day *every day*. Rocks are poor conductors of heat, so the outside of the rock heats up and expands more than the inside, eventually weakening the rock's outer shell.

When a large rock breaks into smaller pieces, it increases in surface area. In other words, parts of rock that used to be inside the big rock are now the outer surface of the smaller rocks. Weathering processes generally affect the surface of rocks, so weathering has a sort of snowball effect. Initial weathering produces more surface area, and more surface area means more space for the weathering processes to continue their job.

1:14:54

Chemical weathering is the decomposition of rocks and minerals through chemical reactions between the rock and its environment. Chemical weathering processes include:

- **dissolution**
- **oxidation**
- **hydrolysis**

Dissolution is the breakdown of minerals into their component elements. Most minerals don't dissolve very much in pure water, but add a little acid to that water, and much more mineral dissolves. Since a rock is composed of minerals, it also breaks down in the presence of acid. Limestone just flat-out dissolves in the presence of acid, so acid rain has caused some serious destruction of limestone.

NATURAL RAINFALL IS WEAKLY ACIDIC, EVEN IF IT'S NOT CONSIDERED ACID RAIN. SEE OTHER IMPORTANT STUFF TO LEARN MORE ABOUT IT.

Life is too short to stuff a mushroom.

– Storm Jameson

Oxidation is really just rusting. It's a reaction involving oxygen (often oxygen dissolved in water). Oxidation is the chemical process most likely to weather iron-containing minerals, like the ferromagnesian minerals olivine and pyroxene. Remember, ferromagnesian minerals are mafic, which means they contain plenty of iron and magnesium. The iron in these minerals is released by dissolution and reacts with oxygen to form a reddish-brown oxide called **hematite** or a yellowish-brown hydroxide called **limonite**. Reddish soils and sedimentary rocks may contain small bits of hematite or limonite.

Minerals containing lots of silica, on the other hand, are most likely dissolved by a process called **hydrolysis**. In short, hydrolysis is just the term for the reaction of a mineral with water.

HYDROLYSIS IS EASY TO REMEMBER BECAUSE YOU PROBABLY KNOW THAT "HYDRO" MEANS "WATER."

Hydrolysis is a special kind of dissolution reaction in which excess protons or hydroxyl ions are left in solution at the end of the reaction. The water's positive hydrogen ions and negative hydroxyl ions react with the ions in the minerals. During hydrolysis, positive hydrogen ions actually replace the positive

ions in the minerals, changing the minerals' composition. The negative hydroxyl ions just get left behind in the solution. This reaction happens most often with silicates like feldspar. Hydrolysis breaks down feldspar into **clay minerals**.

Bowen's reaction series can also help us understand weathering, too. The minerals that crystallize later in the series (like quartz and potassium feldspar, which have lower crystallization temperatures) are more stable in the weathering environment than those that crystallize early in the process (like olivine and pyroxene, which have higher crystallization temperatures). When we say that these later-forming minerals are more stable, we mean that they are less affected by chemical weathering, so they are less likely to react with the elements around them when they are exposed to water and the atmosphere.

1:17:56

A rock's susceptibility to weathering is determined by:

- **structure**
- **environment**

A rock's **structure** is its physical form. If a rock has **joints** or fractures, it's more susceptible to physical weathering such as frost wedging, because the joints and fractures allow water to seep into the rocks. You remember that frost wedging occurs when the water in the cracks freezes and thaws, expanding the cracks in rocks and eventually causing them to break up. Rocks less susceptible to joints and fractures will be less susceptible to frost wedging. So you see, a rock's structure affects how the rock weathers.

Some rocks are predisposed to weathering, but other rocks are a victim of their upbringing. Be kind. Recognize that some rocks are affected by weathering simply because of their environment.

The present **environment** of a rock affects how it weathers, too, in a couple of ways. Higher temperatures speed up reactions, so rocks in a hotter climate are often more weathered than rocks in a cold climate. More important than temperature, however, is the abundance of water in the environment.

When a higher flux of water moves through the environment, more mineral can dissolve, or hydrolyze, so more weather occurs. **Rain water** is a very weak acid that dissolves rock, and the **bipolar water molecule** itself is a chemical weathering agent. Water is also responsible for some physical weathering like frost wedging.

There is no gravity. The Earth sucks.

– Graffito

The topography (physical features) of the land around the rock influences weathering as well. An exposed rock on a steep mountain is less protected from rain and frost than a rock in a lowland. A rock on a mountainside also has the pull of gravity working on it, causing it to crumble downhill.

1:19:57

When rocks weather, they break down into little pieces. **Erosion** is the process by which the little pieces of weathered rock get carried off and scattered around. There are several agents of erosion:

- **wind**
- **water**
- **ice**
- **gravity**

All of these agents contribute to the physical breakdown (weathering) and movement of particles (transportation) causing erosion.

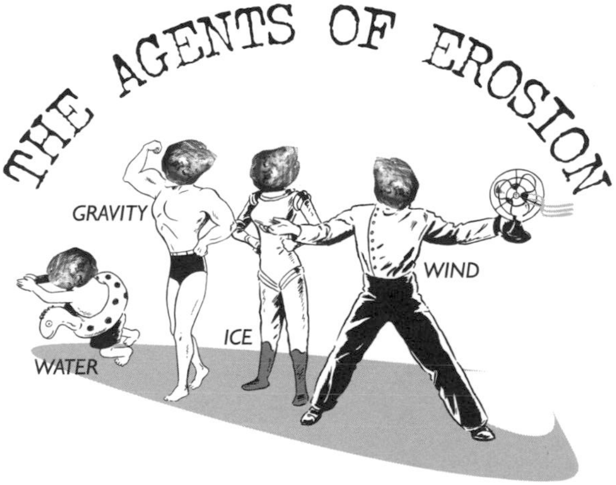

VIDEO NOTES

VI

Mass wasting is the general downhill movement of soil, mud, and rocks under the influence of gravity.

Weathering breaks things into smaller pieces, then the agents of erosion get a hold of the materials and, aided by the force of gravity, it all slides downhill. By the way, the hill doesn't have to be steep at all for this to happen. In fact, sometimes mass wasting happens on land that is nearly level. When the downhill movement happens slowly, like at a rate of 1 to 10 millimeters per year, it's called **creep**. When the downhill slide happens quickly, we call it an **avalanche**, a **mudslide**, or a **landslide**.

WATCH FOR FALLING ROCKS

MORE CRUSTY STUFF:

BELIEVE IT OR NOT, IN THE LONG RUN, CREEP USUALLY CAUSES MORE OVERALL PROPERTY DAMAGE THAN LANDSLIDES DO.

Into the mud, scum queen.

– The Man with Two Brains

In a **rock fall**, individual rocks loosened by chemical and physical weathering fall from a steep mountainside or cliff to the ground below.

In some cold regions, the top layers of soil freeze and thaw, and the underlying layers stay frozen solid. The freezing and thawing upper layers tend to stay saturated with water, and when they thaw, they slide downhill over the frozen layers. When saturated layers of upper soil ooze downhill over frozen layers, they carry debris and junk downhill with them. This phenomenon is called **solifluction**. Solifluction contributes to mass wasting.

SUMMARY

- Weathering is the mechanical disintegration and chemical alteration of the rocks on the Earth's surface. There are two types of weathering:
  - **physical**
  - **chemical**

- Physical weathering, also called mechanical weathering, breaks rocks up into smaller pieces. Physical weathering processes include:
  - **frost wedging**
  - **exfoliation**
  - **thermal expansion and contraction**

Video Notes

- Chemical weathering decomposes rock through chemical reactions between the rock and its environment. Chemical weathering processes include:
    - **dissolution**
    - **oxidation**
    - **hydrolysis**

- Physical and chemical weathering occur simultaneously.

- A rock's susceptibility to weathering is determined by both its structure (physical form) and by its environmental conditions.

Check out This Other Important Stuff:

For more on weathering and acid rain, see **OTHER IMPORTANT STUFF 8**, page 236.

Quiz 6

1. What two environmental factors are needed to produce frost wedging?

2. What mechanical weathering process would take place in a desert?

3. What are the three main types of chemical weathering?

4. What are the two types of weathering?

5. How does temperature affect weathering?

6. What is dissolution?

7. What is the dominant force in mass wasting?

8. Mechanical weathering changes a rock's minerals. True or False?

Quiz

9. What three processes are part of erosion?

10. What are the "agents of erosion"?

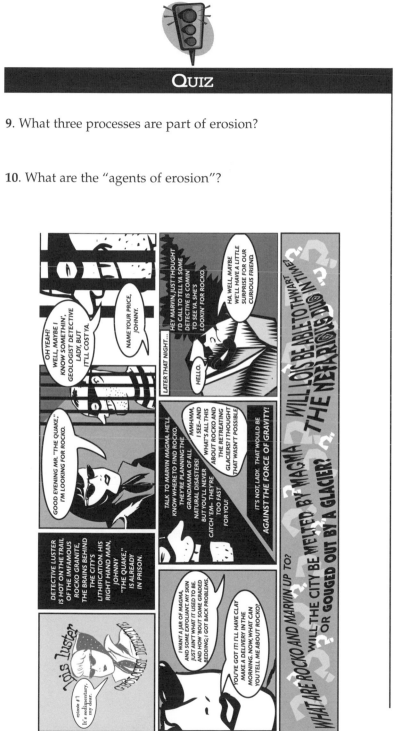

1:23:28

Section D: Sedimentation and Sedimentary Rocks

Sedimentary Rocks

The word "sedimentary" comes from the Latin word *sedimentum*, which means "settling." Sedimentum literally refers to solid material that settles out of a liquid. This is the way most sedimentary rocks are originally deposited: little weathered pieces of existing rocks we call **sediment** erode and are deposited in valleys, seas, lakes, and (most importantly) the ocean. As more and more sediment gets deposited, the earlier layers of sediment get buried and compacted together. Eventually, due to the pressure of burial, the deep sediment is cemented together and forms solid rocks.

1:24:28

Sedimentary rocks are an important part of **the rock cycle**. The rock cycle shows the interrelationship of the three fundamental rock types, and explains the existence and formation of each. There are three fundamental rock types:

- Sedimentary rocks.
- Igneous, the rocks that form from cooling lava or magma.
- **Metamorphic rocks**, which form from pre-existing sedimentary, igneous, or even metamorphic rocks altered by heat, pressure and **migrating fluids**.

We'll talk more about metamorphic rocks later. Now let's look at how all these rocks are related to each other in the rock cycle.

VIDEO NOTES

VI

Here's how the rock cycle works:

1 Rocks that are not buried beneath the surface weather, erode, and form sediments.

2 These sediments accumulate in deposits that pile onto each other and cement together into solid sedimentary rocks. The solid sedimentary rocks are composed of little pieces of weathered and eroded rocks.

3 The sedimentary rocks are buried and subjected to intense pressure, heat, and migrating fluids which cause chemical reactions between the little pieces. This metamorphic process will change the sedimentary rocks, turning them into metamorphic rocks.

4 Upon exposure to even higher temperatures, the metamorphic rocks melt back into magma. The magma cools, forms igneous rocks, and the rock cycle starts over again.

Sediments, sedimentary rocks, igneous rocks, and metamorphic rocks can all be re-weathered into sediments without completing the whole cycle.

The sediment in sedimentary rocks comes from solid rock particles produced by weathering rocks. These particles are called **clastic** materials, and the accumulation of clastic materials is called **clastic sediment**.

PAPER OR CLASTIC?
ICE

1:26:16

Clastic sedimentary rocks are primarily classified by the grain sizes of their component clastic materials. There are three general categories of sedimentary rocks:

- **conglomerates**
- **sandstones**
- **mudstones**

Sedimentary rocks made of clowns
Clownstone

Sedimentary rocks composed of large, rounded clastic sediments are called **conglomerate** sedimentary rocks. The large sediments that make up conglomerates include:

- **boulders**
- **cobbles**
- **pebbles**
- **granules**

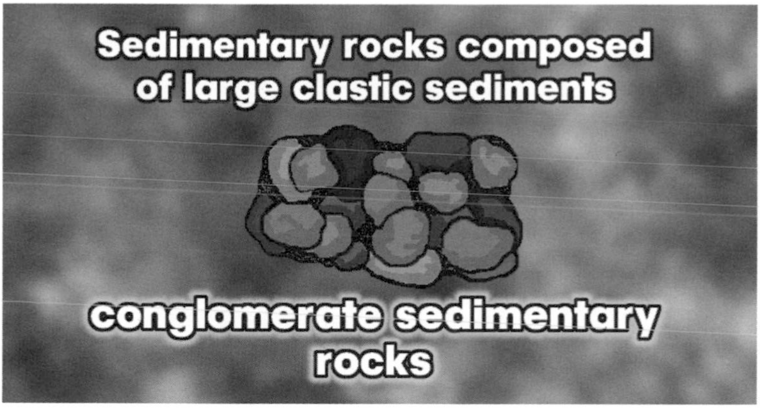
Sedimentary rocks composed of large clastic sediments
conglomerate sedimentary rocks

Back off, man, I'm a scientist.

– Igon in *Ghostbusters*

Each of these sediment types is larger than 2 millimeters in diameter. Smaller clastic sediments between $\frac{1}{16}^{th}$ of a millimeter and 2 millimeters are called **sand**. A sedimentary rock made up of sand is called **sandstone**, logically enough.

Sedimentary rocks made up of sand
Sandstone

The third type of sedimentary rocks, mudstones, are made of clastic sediments smaller than $\frac{1}{16}$th of a millimeter in diameter.

These tiny sediments are called silt and clay and cannot be seen with the naked eye. Mudstones are composed of both silt and clay in approximately equal proportions. Mudstones can be further subdivided into siltstone and shale.

- **Siltstones**: Sedimentary rocks made only of silt are called siltstone. Silt is sediment between $\frac{1}{16}$th and $\frac{1}{256}$th of a millimeter in diameter.

- **Shale**: Sedimentary rock composed of **clay-sized particle**s. Clay is sediment smaller than $\frac{1}{256}$th of a millimeter.

You can tell a bit about the environment in which sedimentary rocks formed by the size of the component sediments. Sediments are mostly moved around by water. It takes a lot more energy to move big stones than small ones. A big, fast-moving river might be able to carry a good-sized rock, but a slow little trickle can only carry tiny sediments like silt.

Siltstone can form around stagnant **lagoons**, where there is no fast, energetic current to carry in large particles and add to the bed of sediments. The sluggish water only brings in tiny sediments. Conglomerates, which are composed of large clastic sediments, form near sources of higher energy such as fast-moving rivers. A strong current can carry large sediments along for some distance before the sediments settle out and collect in deposits.

1:29:16

Chemical sedimentary rocks form from the weathered remains of other rocks that were dissolved during the weathering process. Chemical sedimentary rocks also form from materials in solution produced by weathering sea shells and other components of the environment that break down. As rocks, shells, and the remains of plants and animals weather, they produce ions that dissolve into the water and wash into lakes and oceans. If these dissolved ions later precipitate (separate) out of the solution they formed with the water, they can form mineral particles. These particles accumulate as chemical sediments, eventually forming what we call chemical sedimentary rocks.

Unlike clastic sedimentary rocks, which are classified by the size of their component particles, chemical sedimentary rocks are classified by their chemical composition. For example, **carbonate** rocks are chemical sedimentary rocks primarily made up of **calcium carbonate**, or $CaCO_3$, which is also known as the mineral calcite. **Limestone** is a carbonate rock composed of calcium carbonate.

Chemical sedimentary rocks also include **evaporites**. It's easy to remember how evaporites form—Here's the story. Evaporating sea water leaves behind deposits which **lithify** (harden) into sedimentary rocks. So, sea water *evaporates* to form *evaporites*. Common evaporites contain halite, which is sodium chloride (rock salt), and gypsum, which is calcium sulfate.

1:31:07

Coal is a **biochemical sedimentary rock**. It's called biochemical because it forms from organic sedimentation, which is the weathering remains of plants and animals. The partially decomposed animal and plant remains, called **peat**, accumulates and

is eventually buried and transformed into rock. Limestone (**chalk**) made up of the shells of marine animals is also a biochemical sedimentary rock.

1:31:27

The environment in which rocks form is called the **paleoenvironment**. There is a whole variety of important paleoenvironments where sedimentary rocks form:

- **Fluvial environments**, which are found in and around rivers.
- **Deltaic environments**, which, like the Mississippi delta, are fan-shaped deposit areas at the mouths of rivers.
- **Desert environments**, which have less than 10 inches of rainfall per year.
- **Glacial environments**, which we'll discuss later in Section C, "Earth Surface Processes."
- **Shallow marine environments,** which are areas where sediment is deposited between the shore and the edge of the **continental shelf** (sometimes as much as 400 kilometers offshore).
- **Lacustrine environments**, which are stagnant lagoons and lakes.
- **Beach environments**, which are shorelines made of sand and pebbles, dude.

- **Turbidite environments**, which are deposits on underwater marine slopes.
- **Pelagic environments**, where you find deep, open ocean sediments.

Sedimentary rocks are deposited in layers. These layers may differ from one another in composition. When the layers of materials lithify (solidify) into rock, they form stripe-like layers called **bedding** or **stratification**. You can tell a lot about a sedimentary rock's paleoenvironment by looking at the rock's stratification. Check out a rock's stripes for: 1:32:30

- **Cross-bedding**
- **Ripple marks**
- **Graded bedding**

Layers inclined at an angle to the main **bedding planes** are called **cross-bedding**. Cross-bedding indicates that wind or water was the agent that deposited the sediment. The cross-beds incline downward in the direction of the flow of wind or water, since they were pushed in that direction.

The cherry tomato is a marvelous invention, producing as it does a satisfactorily explosive squish when bitten.

– Miss Manners

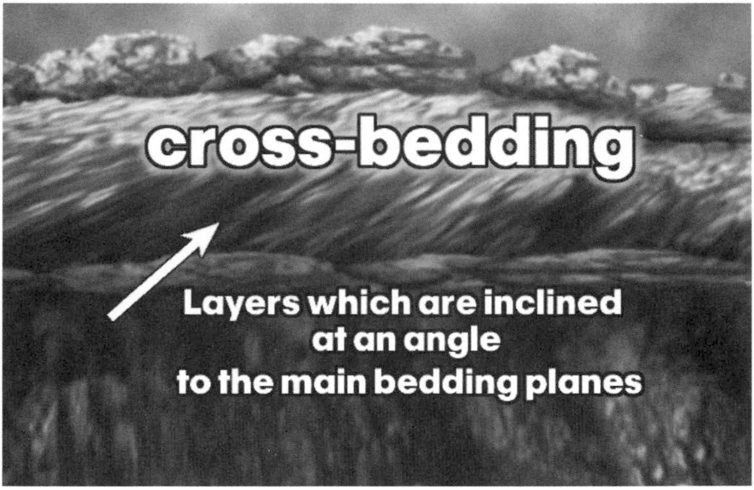
cross-bedding
Layers which are inclined
at an angle
to the main bedding planes

Ripple marks are low, narrow ridges preserved on sedimentary rocks (generally sandstones), which look like a rippled water surface. You can tell by looking at the ripple marks whether the rock formed in water whose current moved in one direction, or in water in which the waves moved to and fro.

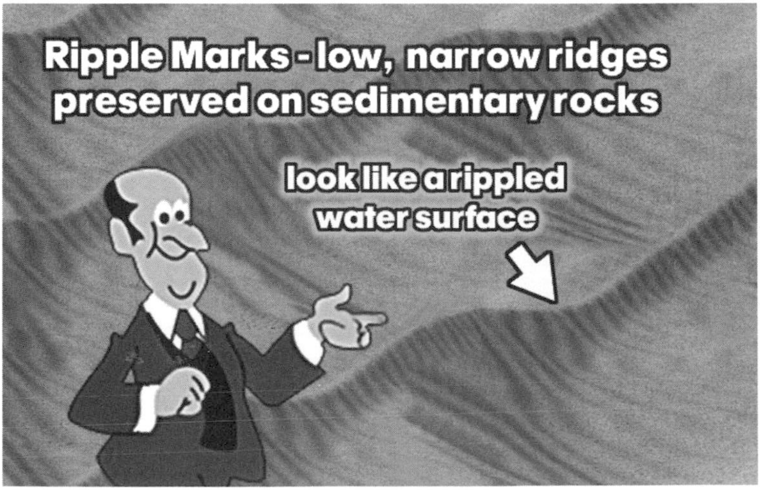
Ripple Marks - low, narrow ridges
preserved on sedimentary rocks
look like a rippled
water surface

Graded bedding is bedding in which the size of the clastic sediments changes. For example, the clasts in a stratified sedimentary rock might go from cobble-sized at the bottom to fine-grained sand at the top. Graded bedding indicates that the rock formed in an environment in which the energy changed over time. For example, a stream might be fast-moving and leave deposits of large cobbles in a bed. Over time its current gets weaker and the size of the clastic material deposited by the stream gets smaller and smaller. After a while, the energy of the stream isn't strong enough to carry large sediments any more. Graded bedding commonly forms during a flood.

Evidence of **mud cracks** in sedimentary rocks also tells you something about the environment in which the rocks were formed. Mud cracks form in dried-out, clay-rich sediment. If you see preserved, polygonal-shaped mud cracks in a sedimentary rock, you know that the rock formed in an area that dries out periodically, like the **flood plain** of a river.

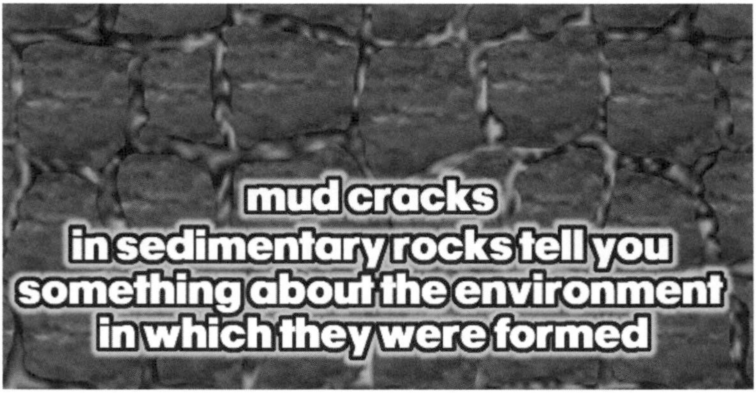
mud cracks
in sedimentary rocks tell you
something about the environment
in which they were formed

1:34:27

Sedimentary facies are the physical, chemical and biological characteristics a sedimentary rock gets from its environment. Think of the term "facies" as "characteristics." The rock's facies are its visible shape, texture, and internal components which may be attributed to the environment in which the rock was formed.

Marine transgression and marine regression affect the facies of sedimentary rocks forming just off the sea shore.

Marine Transgression
when sea covers land
on a continent that used
to be exposed to the air

Marine transgression occurs when the sea moves onto the land. In other words, the shoreline moves inland, covering more of the land (bummer for humans, cool for fish.) During a marine transgression, deeper water sediments cover sediments that were deposited in shallow water. The deep water sediments (mudstone or limestone) are different from the sediments that get

deposited closer to shore (sandstone). This difference shows up in the facies, or internal and external characteristics, of the sedimentary rocks.

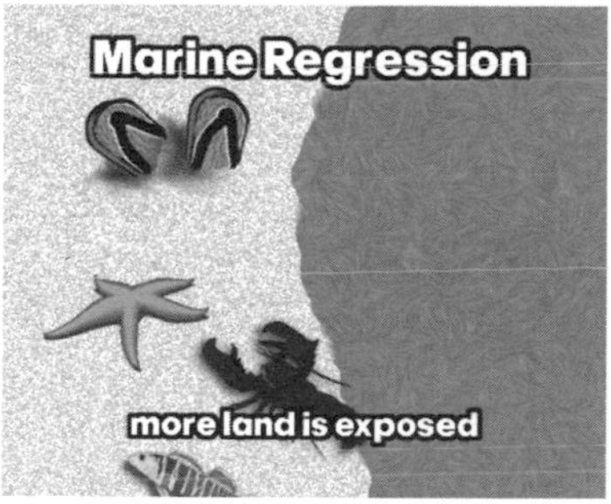

Marine regression is the opposite of marine transgression. In marine regression, the shoreline moves further out so more land is exposed. The effects of marine regression also show up in the composition of the layers of sedimentary rocks formed in the area. The sediments deposited in deeper water are covered by sediments deposited in shallower water; the sedimentary facies reflect this change in sediment composition.

Keep in mind that there's no single indicator that will tell you beyond the shadow of a doubt where or how a rock was formed. Geologists rely on a combination of clues and sources for answers.

Quiz 7

1. A first-year student finds a rock. It has rounded, sand-sized grains. He correctly assumes the rock's past environment was a __________ .

2. A geologist is mapping and she finds crossbeds. In which two environments could this rock have been deposited? If she later finds a marine fossil and the beds are only 2″ high, which of the two environments should she choose?

3. Describe how the environment of a sedimentary rock can produce certain facies. Give an example.

4. Clastic sedimentary rocks are classified first by their __________.

5. A wildcatter drilling for oil finds limestone above shale above sandstone. From this he assumes a marine (transgression/regression) occurred in the past.

6. Can minerals in an igneous rock become part of a sedimentary rock? Explain.

Quiz

7. Name two chemical sedimentary rocks.

8. What type of sedimentary rock is coal?

9. During a marine regression the shoreline moves __________.

10. Draw all components of the rock cycle.

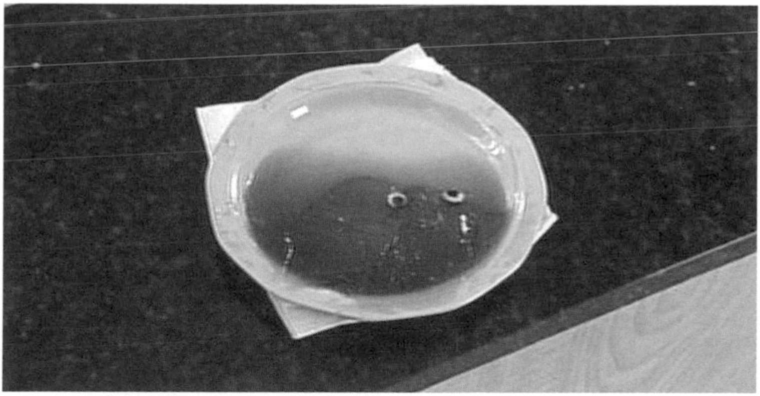

AUTHENTIC PHOTOGRAPH OF BILLY THE AMORPHOUS BOY

PRACTICE EXAM I

1. The three most recent eras of geological time (youngest to oldest) are

   A) Cenozoic, Mesozoic, Paleozoic

   B) Mesozoic, Paleozoic, Cenozoic

   C) Recent, Tertiary, and Quaternary

   D) Paleozoic, Proterozoic, Archean

   E) Cenozoic, Archean, Paleozoic

2. The geological time scale is based on

   A) absolute time and relevant time

   B) relative time and obsolete time

   C) absolute time and relative time

   D) relative time and relative fossils

   E) absolute time and deep time

3. Placing geological events in a chronological sequence by observing the rock record is called

   A) principle dating

   B) uncle dating

   C) relative dating

   D) radioactive dating

   E) normal dating

TEST YOURSELF

4. Most sedimentary rocks are deposited in flat-lying layers. This idea is called the Principle of

   A) Uniformitarianism

   B) Faunal Dating

   C) Metamorphism

   D) Lateral Continuity

   E) Superposition

5. Which one of the following cases is an example of the Law of Superposition?

   A) intrusive igneous rocks

   B) plutonic rocks

   C) contact metamorphic rocks

   D) overturned sedimentary rocks

   E) flat-lying sedimentary rocks

6. The Principle of Uniformitarianism includes

   A) events that are sudden and catastrophic

   B) geological events that occur slowly

   C) ice ages and meteor impacts

   D) modern processes

   E) all the above

It's economically unsound to grow up.

– *Nothing in Common*

7. Most minerals belong to the silicate group because

   A) they are the hardest minerals known to man.

   B) oxygen and silicon are the two most abundant minerals in the crust.

   C) silicates only form simple structures, not chains or sheets.

   D) they have a tendency to cleave along a smooth plane.

   E) many other compounds are chemically impossible to form.

8. The hardest and softest minerals on the Mohs scale of hardness are

   A) diamond and graphite.

   B) quartz and feldspar.

   C) graphite and quartz.

   D) diamond and talc.

   E) diamond and ruby.

9. Cleavage is produced by

   A) big elements in a mineral.

   B) heating up all minerals.

   C) a plane of weak bonds in the mineral.

   D) breaking all minerals.

   E) the absence of bonds in the mineral.

TEST YOURSELF

10. The mineral olivine is considered a

    A) ferromagnesian mineral.

    B) felsic mineral.

11. A fine-grained igneous rock cooled ________ and ________ the crust.

    A) both rapidly, slowly in

    B) slowly, at the surface of

    C) slowly, deep within

    D) rapidly, at the surface of

    E) rapidly, deep within

12. Sills are

    A) always porphyritic.

    B) concordant tabular bodies.

    C) huge irregular shaped bodies.

    D) discordant tabular bodies.

    E) discordant, mushroom-shaped intrusive bodies.

13. Bowen's reaction series explains

    A) how a magma can have the same composition at many different temperatures.

    B) how felsic magma can be formed from mafic magma.

    C) how all magma were once felsic.

    D) the enrichment of magma in Fe and Mg.

    E) the difference between fine-grained and coarse-grained igneous rocks.

14. Mechanical weathering

    A) chemically disintegrates the rock.

    B) dissolves calcium in limestone rocks.

    C) forms carbonic acid.

    D) rounds the surfaces of the rock.

    E) breaks the rock into smaller pieces.

15. Sediment becomes a sedimentary rock by the process of ____________, which involves the ___________ of grains, loss of water, and _________.

    A) cementation, rounding, calcite

    B) precipitation, sorting, cementation

    C) evaporation, crystallization, gypsum

    D) lithification, transportation, chert

    E) lithification, compaction, cementation

16. A geologist is studying a section of rock from a bore hole. At the bottom she finds limestone, then further up, a section of mudstone grading into sandstone. From this data she infers

    A) that the ocean was moving onto the land.

    B) that if she drills down farther she will find coal.

    C) that mountains were far from the depositional area.

    D) that the ocean is moving off the land.

    E) that a glacier flowed over the area.

TEST YOURSELF

17. Sedimentary rocks are classified as

    A) chemical and mechanical.

    B) clastic and chemical.

    C) biological and physical.

    D) seasonal and chemical.

    E) clastic and plastic.

STRESS RELIEF

A Short List of Fun Things to Do with a Rock

1. Paint it like an egg and put it in the fridge. Watch a frustrated victim try to make an omelet with it.
2. Treat it to a ritzy night out on the town. Be sure both of you dress up snazzily.
3. Replace the regular coffee in a fancy restaurant with it.
4. Stone wash your jeans.
5. Stone wash your car.
6. Stone wash behind your ears.
7. Arrange for it to spend the night in the White House Lincoln bedroom.
8. Go to a bad part of town wearing a cape and tights. Claim you are the "Granite Vigilante." Throw it at a hoodlum. Run.
9. Liken yourself to it in a song. Get sued by Paul Simon.
10. Add "Y" to the end of it and market it as a slow-witted Italian prize fighter.
11. Use it as a toothbrush when you're "roughing it."

THE CEREBELLUM WRITERS' DREAM OFFICE

Due to changes in labor laws, the Writing Department's writers have drafted a list of items for their Ideal Writing Department Office...

- ***hat rack***
- ***round throw rug***
- ***glow-in-the-dark stars and planets***
- ***a 50-gallon drum filled with large binder clips***
- ***beanbag chairs***
- ***2 Nerf hoops for full-court play***
- ***something to play music on (preferably a radio, but a pump organ would do)***
- ***movie posters, animation art***
- ***coffee table***
- ***fish tank***
- ***fish***
- ***snack machine***
- ***chairs that lean (no leather or imitation leather, please)***
- ***video game system***
- ***one of those glass orbs with static electricity inside***
- ***a slurpee machine***
- ***the power to decide who lives and dies***
- ***a pony***
- ***mechanical parrot that repeats what you say***
- ***Batman bop-bag***
- ***walkie-talkies***
- ***a train to go around the ceiling***
- ***cuckoo clock***
- ***headset phones***
- ***laser-tag guns***
- ***8x10s of various comedians***
- ***blackjack dealer***

Study Sidekick

- ***Holly Hobby oven***
- ***brownie mix***
- ***a waterslide***
- ***Domino Rally Game***
- ***tall-backed Masterpiece Theater chairs***
- ***wastebasket that cheers when you throw stuff in it***
- ***giant metro map***
- ***disco ball***
- ***sound system for private and broadcast listening***
- ***snack bar***
- ***dart board***
- ***comfy couch***
- ***a caricaturist***
- ***unlimited supply of Post-It notes***
- ***red-line to Moscow***
- ***force field to ward off intruders***
- ***globe***
- ***collection of comedy videos***
- ***Writing Department t-shirts***
- ***framed group photo***
- ***weapons: scissors, red pens, whip***
- ***cone of silence***
- ***putting green***
- ***life-size cut-out of Gelila***
- ***water cooler***
- ***strobe light***
- ***Venus flytrap***
- ***library (books for research, pleasure, self-development)***
- ***a chicken in every pot***
- ***bikepath from Denmark***

VIDEO TIME CODE

The Rockin' World of Geology Part 2

I. Metamorphism

A. Causes of Metamorphism 0:13:47

1. heat 0:14:50
2. pressure 0:15:15
3. fluid 0:15:43

B. Types of Metamorphism 0:16:25

1. contact metamorphism 0:16:42
2. regional metamorphism 0:17:26
3. foliation 0:19:05

II. Faults and Mountain Building or,

Crash and Crunch Factors 0:24:22

A. Stress and Strain 0:25:34

1. folds 0:26:00
2. anatomy of a fold 0:27:24
3. plunging and nonplunging folds 0:30:35
4. eroded folds 0:31:47

B. Fractures 0:35:17

1. joints 0:36:08

0:36:20 ....2. faults

0:44:39 III. The Earth's Interior and Plate Tectonics

0:44:46 ....A. Seismology and the Earth's Interior

0:44:50 ....1. earthquakes

0:45:01 ....2. elastic rebound theory

0:45:22 ....3. focus

0:45:33 ....4. epicenter

0:45:40 ....5. seismic waves

0:48:48 ....6. Richter magnitude scale

0:50:55 ....7. modified Mercalli scale

0:52:25 ....8. the Earth's interior

0:56:05 ....B. Plate Tectonics

0:56:32 ....1. the theory of continental drift

0:56:55 ....2. Pangea

0:59:18 ....3. sea-floor spreading

1:00:01 ....4. plate boundaries

1:02:45 IV. Earth Surface Processes

1:02:52 ....A. River Systems

1:02:55 ....1. the hydrologic cycle

1:03:42 ....2. runoff

1:04:38 ....3. competence

1:04:56 ....4. stream sediments

1:07:01 ....5. deltas

Video Time Code

V2

6. alluvial fans 1:08:52

7. meandering streams 1:09:23

8. oxbow lakes 1:09:33

9. drainage basin 1:09:55

10. drainage systems 1:10:05

11. headward erosion 1:12:28

12. stream piracy 1:13:09

13. superposition 1:13:36

14. downcutting 1:15:06

15. lateral erosion 1:15:32

B. Shoreline Systems 1:16:46

1. shorelines 1:16:51

2. waves 1:17:05

3. wave refraction 1:18:38

4. longshore currents 1:19:15

5. beaches 1:19:31

6. sand bars 1:19:38

C. Glaciers 1:21:59

1. valley glaciers 1:24:16

2. continental glaciers 1:24:29

3. ice caps 1:25:04

4. glacial movement 1:25:50

5. glacial erosion 1:26:55

STUDY SIDEKICK

VIDEO NOTES

The Rockin' World of Geology Part 2

Metamorphism

0:13:47

Section A: Causes of Metamorphism

It gets hot, deep in the Earth's crust. Sometimes it's so hot and the pressure is so enormous that the rocks melt back into magma. Even when it's not hot enough to melt the rocks, frequently the heat and pressure are still great enough to cause the rocks to grow a new set of minerals, change their texture, and become a new type of rock. When rocks undergo these changes, we say they are **metamorphosed**. Here come the **metamorphic rocks**!

There are three primary causes of metamorphism:

- **heat**
- **pressure**
- **fluids**

0:14:50

Energy within the Earth can be released as **heat**. Applying heat speeds up chemical reactions such as the breaking of chemical bonds and the formation of new minerals. Rocks exposed to lots of heat will metamorphose so they contain a **mineral assemblage** that is more stable at high temperatures. In other words, rocks exposed to high temperatures will change their **mineralogy** and texture until they take on a form that can withstand the heat.

0:15:15

Pressure is another factor in metamorphism. Buried rocks are subjected to pressure from the weight of all the rocks on top of them in addition to the increase in temperature. The deeper the rocks are buried, the higher the pressure. The mineral grains in a buried rock may pack more closely together or grow larger as a result of pressure. The original minerals in the buried rock also may change into a new group of minerals stable at the higher pressures and temperatures. Geologists call this process of forming new minerals from old minerals **recrystallization**.

0:15:43

The presence of fluids, such as water containing dissolved ions in solution, is another factor influencing the formation of metamorphic rocks. Like heat, the presence of a fluid can increase the rate of metamorphic reactions. The fluid consists of water and carbon dioxide, and is usually present in areas where metamorphism is occurring. The fluid also contains other ions that

move freely through the metamorphic fluid and speed up the rate of chemical reactions acting on the rocks. In many cases, the movement of the metamorphic fluid and its dissolved ions will alter the composition of the rocks.

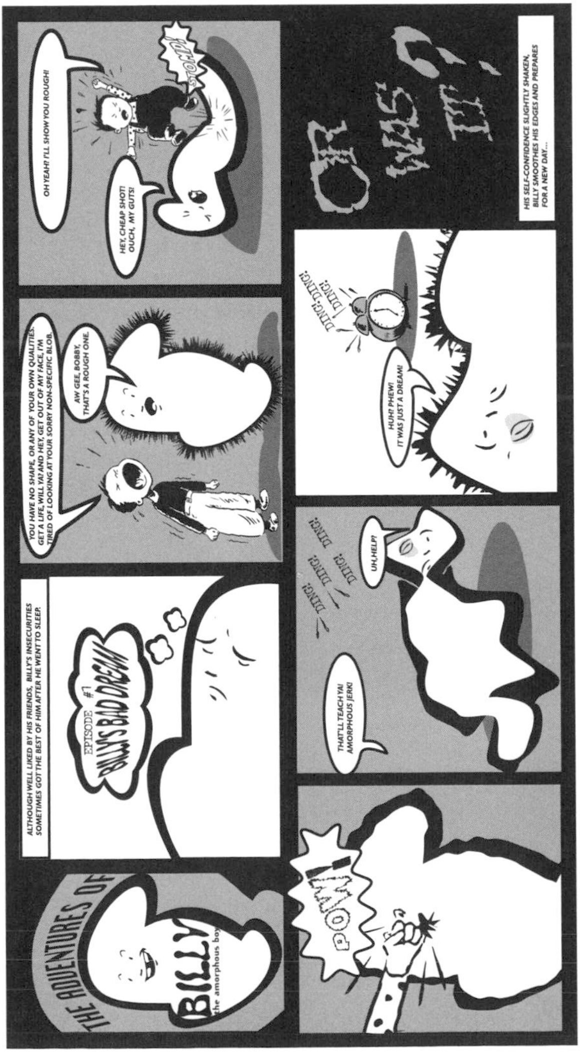

Quiz

Quiz 8

> I coalesce the vapor of human experience into a viable and logical comprehension.
>
> – Mel Brooks, *The History of the World Part One*

1. If we increase the temperature during metamorphism, how is the rate of reaction affected?

2. Can the components of a metamorphic rock ever be part of a sedimentary rock? Explain.

3. What are the two main components of the fluid associated with metamorphism?

4. What do geologists call the formation of new minerals from old minerals?

Section B: Types of Metamorphism

0:16:25 We will discuss two types of metamorphism:

- **contact metamorphism**
- **regional metamorphism**

We distinguish one from the other by the size of the heat source causing the metamorphism.

0:16:42 Metamorphism caused by hot magma intruding into an existing rock is called **contact metamorphism**. Igneous intrusions or plutons form when hot magma intrudes into a bed of existing rock. Geologists call the existing rock **country rock**. Contact metamorphism occurs at the boundary between the hot pluton and the country rock. During contact metamorphism, the hot, intruding magma comes into contact with the country rock, and the heat from the intruding magma heats the country rock enough for the country rock to metamorphose. The part of the country rock that metamorphoses as a result of its contact with the magma is referred to as an **aureole**. The size of a contact aureole ranges from several meters to several kilometers.

0:17:26 **Regional metamorphism** occurs when high pressures and temperatures affect huge areas of the Earth's crust. Large-scale, regional metamorphism occurs when **tectonic plates** (those continent-sized chunks of crust we talked about in *The Rockin' World of Geology Part 1*), bump against each other. The geological processes that occur in the area where two continents crunch against each other can cause huge regions of rock to metamorphose.

Effects of Metamorphism

What actually happens to rocks when the heat, pressure, and fluids metamorphose rocks? New minerals form with different compositions and crystal structures. When the mineralogy and texture changes, the rocks actually change their identity and get new names. For example, shale can turn into **slate**, a considerably harder rock, when it's in an environment of about 200 degrees centigrade.

Metamorphosed rocks look and feel different from how they did before they changed. There is a set of attributes and textures that metamorphosed rocks commonly exhibit, and naturally, these particular attributes and textures all have names.

MY NAME USED TO BE BILL, BUT I'M KNOWN AS GEORGE NOW.

0:19:05

Foliation occurs when a rock undergoing regional metamorphism is affected by heat and pressure. When stress is applied to rocks undergoing metamorphism, the minerals form a pattern or fabric. **Foliation** is the pattern that forms when the minerals align themselves in flat or wavy parallel planes. Foliation produces a texture especially apparent along cleavage planes (the plane where the rock splits or cleaves). You can see foliation, and you can feel it—but you can't smell it, so don't try.

HOWDY!

examples of country rock

There are three specific types of foliation:

- **slaty cleavage**
- **schistosity**
- **gneissosity**

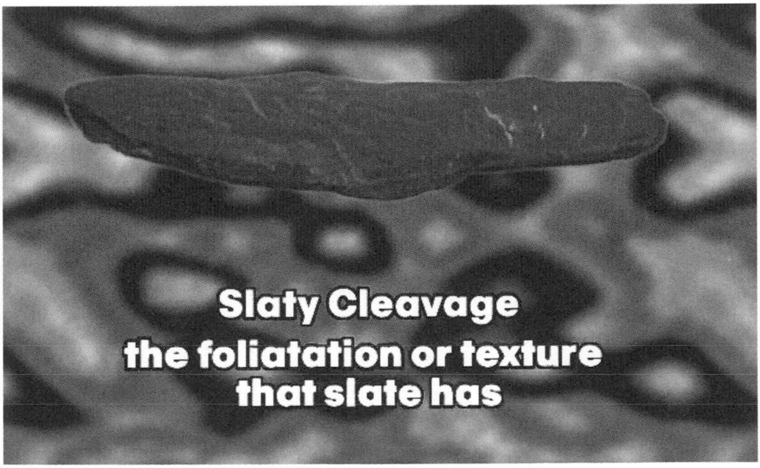
Slaty Cleavage
the foliatation or texture
that slate has

Slaty cleavage is the foliation, or texture, of **slate**. Slate is a metamorphic rock composed of individual mineral grains too small to see unless you magnify them. Slate splits easily along cleavage planes because of the way its crystals are formed. If you run your hand over a piece of slate, you may feel little ridges or bumps that run parallel to each other. This foliated texture is slaty cleavage.

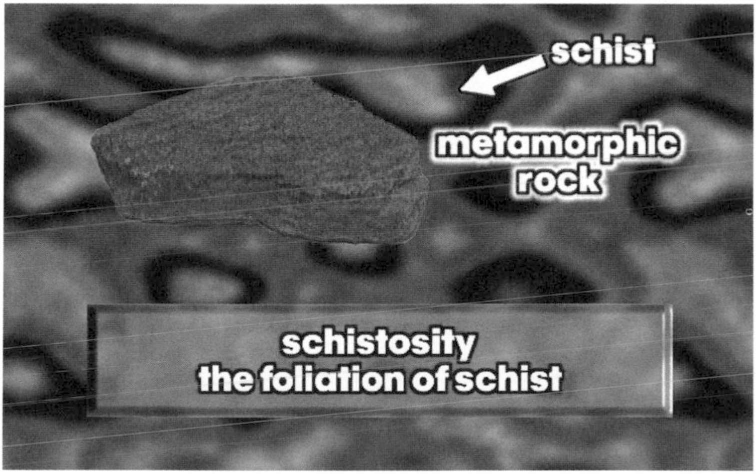

Schistosity, also called **schistose foliation**, is the term used to describe the foliation of **schist**, another type of metamorphic rock. Schist has individual mineral grains large enough to be seen without magnifying them. Over half of the minerals in schist are flattened and platy, or elongated and rod-like in shape. There are different types of schist, and each type is known by its component mineral that lends the rock its most conspicuous characteristics. For example, biotite schist is distinguished by its dark bands of biotite mica. The mineral alignment of schist produces schistosity. Schistosity looks

scaly and wavy. On the fresh surface that is exposed when the rock is split, it is clear that flattened, platy minerals are organized parallel to each other.

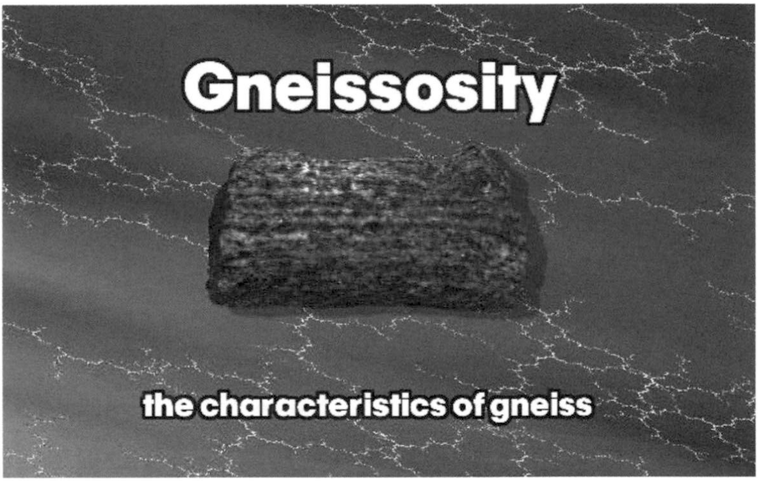

Gneissosity describes the characteristics of **gneiss**. Gneiss is metamorphic rock with large, granular minerals, and visible light and dark bands. The segregation of minerals into light and dark bands is even more prominent in gneiss than in schist; the bands form an irregular pattern that makes gneiss rocks look streaked. Isn't that nice?

Metamorphic rocks without foliation, lineation, or directional texture are called **hornfels**. The texture of hornfels is called **hornfelsic** or **granular**. Any flat or elongated minerals in these rocks are oriented randomly. Foliation is caused by stress or directed pressure, which causes minerals to line up parallel to each other in schist and gneiss. Hornfels commonly form during contact metamorphism. During this process, the metamorphosed rock is changed by the heat of intruding magma, but there is little stress to cause mineral alignment. Heat without stress or directed pressure may metamorphose rock, but it doesn't line the minerals up in a linear or planar fashion.

SUMMARY

- The two main types of metamorphism are regional and contact metamorphism.
- Metamorphic rocks are classified by their texture.
- The two main textures of metamorphic rock are foliated and hornfelsic (granular).
- Foliated metamorphic rocks include:
    1. slate
    2. schist
    3. gneiss

- Foliated metamorphic rocks are described by at least one of the following characteristics:

  1. Slaty cleavage, which means the rock can easily split along cleavage planes. The planes often have bumpy parallel ridges.

  2. Schistosity, which is scaly foliation composed of large-grained minerals you can see without magnifying.

  3. Gneissosity, the coarsest type of foliation, is characterized by alternating bands of light and dark minerals.

- Hornfelsic (granular) metamorphic rocks are characterized by coarse or fine interlocking minerals not aligned in any particular direction or fashion.

Quiz 9

1. What is foliation?

2. What are the two main types of metamorphism?

3. What do geologists call the existing rock surrounding an igneous intrusion?

4. List and briefly describe the three types of foliation.

5. A geologist sees regionally metamorphosed rocks in the middle of Canada, in an area nowhere near a present-day tectonic plate boundary. What could he say about the past? What fundamental principle would he use?

6. Would you expect the contact metamorphic rock zones around a pluton to follow the Principle of Lateral Continuity? Explain.

Who the hell wants to hear actors talk?

— H.M. Warner, Warner Brothers, 1927

0:24:22

Faults and Mountain Building or, the Crash and Crunch Factors

0:25:34

Section A: Stress and Strain

Any chunk of land that stands significantly higher than the land around it is considered a mountain. That may seem like a rather vague definition of "mountain," but it's appropriately vague. Mountains come in a variety of sizes and shapes, and there are a number of processes that can contribute to mountain building. Geologists call mountain building **orogenesis**. In *The Rockin' World of Geology Part 1*, we talked about volcanoes, which are, of course, mountains formed by molten rock that spews out through the Earth's crust and hardens. Volcanism is one form of orogenesis. Folding and faulting are two more processes that can build mountains.

THE STUDY OF FOLDING AND FAULTING IS CALLED STRUCTURAL GEOLOGY AND THE PROCESS OF FOLDING AND FAULTING IS CALLED TECTONICS.

Many ancient rocks have been twisted and contorted since their formation. There are a number of factors that contribute to rock contortions; the main process is the movement of the continental plates.

VIDEO NOTES

V2

Here are some terms that apply to rock contortions.

- **Stress** refers to the force applied to rock.
- **Strain** is the deformation or change in a rock's shape as a result of stress.

Stress specifically refers to the differential force applied to rock. Stress is different from pressure in the following way: Consider a rock deep within the earth. The overlying rocks are heavy and exert considerable pressure on the rock equally in all directions. If, however, an area nearby is under a lower pressure, there is a directed pressure on the rock to move toward that area. The directed pressure is stress.

0:26:00

A **fold** is a deformed rock bed. It's an example of **strain** or shape-change. Folded rock beds used to be flat but were bent by stress, such as the stress that occurs when two continental plates push up against each other. Most folds form deep down in the Earth. Rocks near the surface are more brittle, so instead of folding, they tend to break when exposed to stress. Sometimes the process of erosion or **uplift** exposes folds so they end up near the surface where we can see them.

There are two types of folds:

- **anticline**
- **synclines**

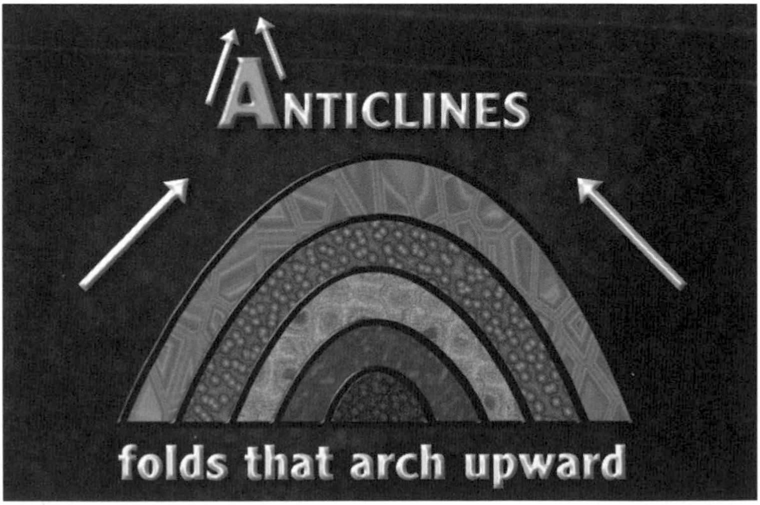

Folds that arch upward are called **anticlines**. Think of the letter A at the beginning of the word "anticline." The upward arch of an anticline is shaped kind of like a capital A.

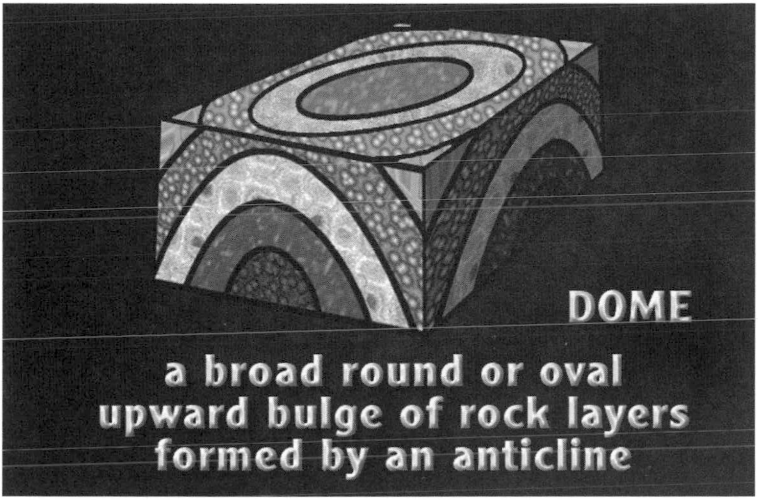
DOME
a broad round or oval upward bulge of rock layers formed by an anticline

A **dome** is a broad, round or oval upward bulge of rock layers formed by an anticline.

Folds that arch downward in the shape of a "U" are called **synclines**. Think of a sink, like the way the beginning of the word "syncline" sounds. The fold of a syncline is shaped a bit like a sink.

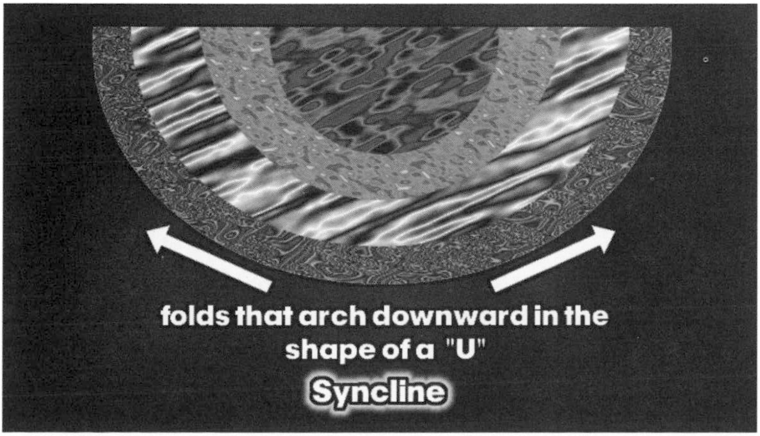
folds that arch downward in the shape of a "U"
Syncline

Mitch: Hi Curly, kill anyone today?

Curly: Day ain't over yet.

– *City Slickers*

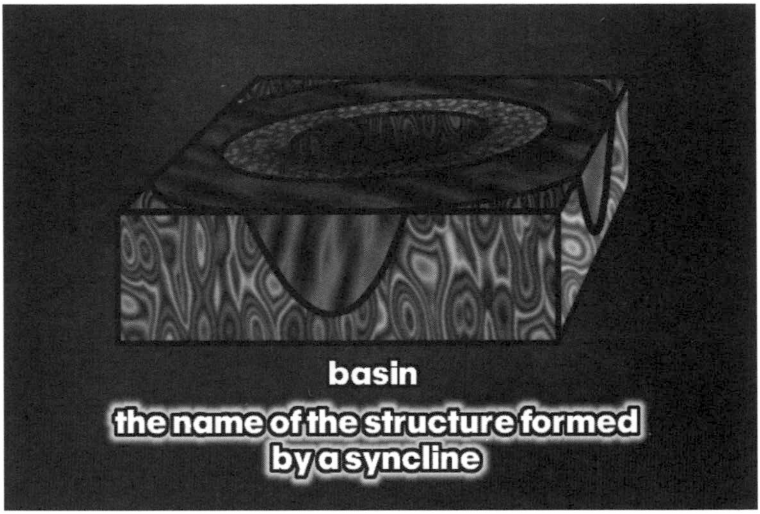

basin
the name of the structure formed by a syncline

A **basin** is a broad, round or oval downward bulge formed by a syncline. Its large bowl shape is the opposite of a dome.

ANTICLINES AND SYNCLINES ARE COMMON GEOLOGICAL STRUCTURES. IT'S ALMOST GUARANTEED THAT THIS STUFF WILL SHOW UP ON YOUR TEST.

Strike and **dip** are terms that describe the orientation of tilted beds of rock. Sediments are deposited horizontally, so if you find a sedimentary rock that is not horizontal, it must have been moved or deformed.

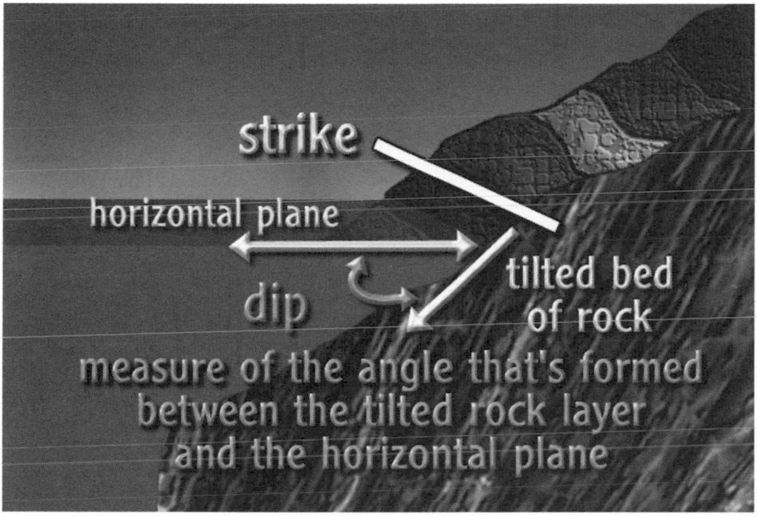

This picture shows a bed of rock that tilts down into the water. The water forms a horizontal plane that meets the rock bed. A line forms where the water meets the tilted rocks. The **strike** is the direction of the line that forms where the tilted rock layer meets a horizontal plane—the surface of the water in this case. In most cases, the geologist estimates an imaginary plane. On geologic maps, the strike is represented by a short line drawn in the direction of the strike.

Dip is the measurement of the angle that forms between a plane of tilted rock layer and a horizontal plane. The rock enters at an angle where it meets the horizontal plane. The angle is measured from an imaginary line running perpendicular to the direction of the strike. On geologic diagrams, the dip is represented by a short line perpendicular to the strike line, and points downhill in the direction of the dip. There's also a number listed beside the symbol to indicate the **dip angle**.

0:27:24

Fold Anatomy

Folds have a number of characteristic features geologists use to describe the geometry of folded structures. The **axial plane** is an imaginary plane that runs down the middle of a fold, dividing it as symmetrically as possible into two equal pieces. An anticline is shaped like a capital A with lots of A's lined up behind it. If you drove a giant blade into the top of the A, dividing it in half, that blade would be the axial plane. Of course it would have to be an imaginary blade, because the axial plane is an imaginary plane.

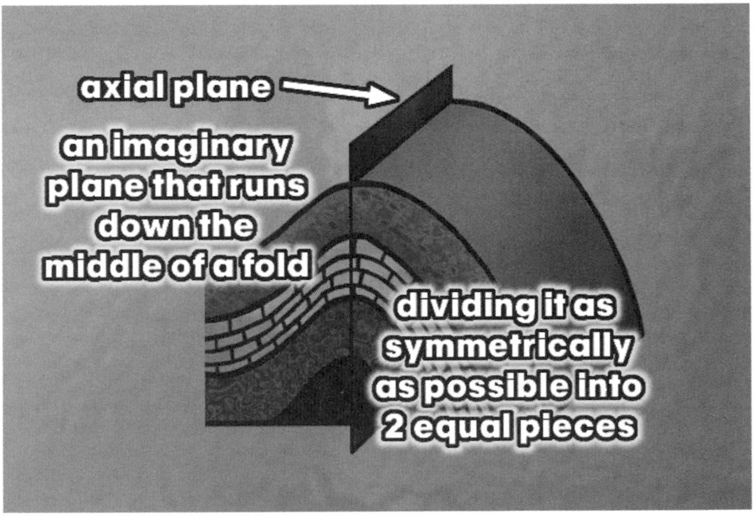

Folds also have what's called a fold **axis**. The axis is not the same thing as the axial plane, although it is a line that lies within the axial plane. The fold axis is a line formed by the intersection of the axial plane and the folded beds. Think of the anticline as an A again. The axial plane runs down the middle of the A, dividing it in half. The axis is the line that forms along the top of the A right where the axial plane bisects the A. The axial plane is a plane; the axis is a line on the plane.

Folds are either **plunging folds** or **nonplunging folds**.

0:30:35

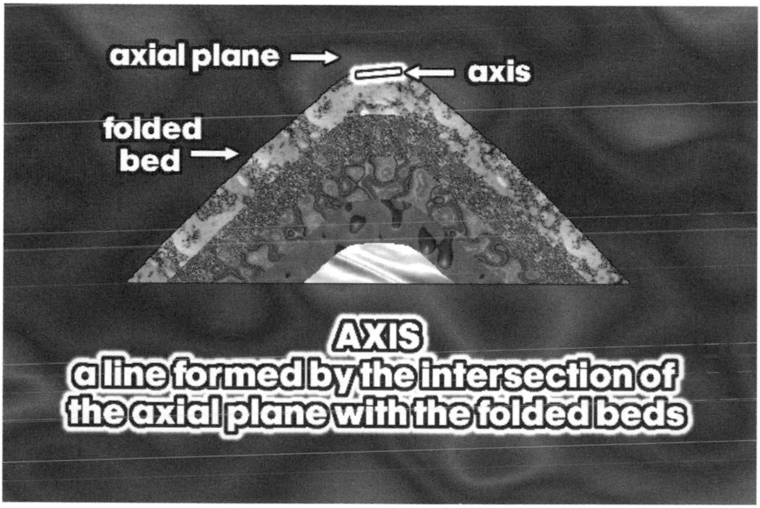

This fold is nonplunging. Notice that the axis is horizontal.

When the axis is *not* horizontal, the fold is a plunging fold. We know that in an anticline, the axial plane bisects the A, and the axis is a line on that plane. Now, let's tilt the A on an incline. Think of a series of A's getting smaller and smaller. The axis follows the top of the A, or the folded bed, so now the axis is no longer perfectly horizontal, it's also inclined. A fold with an axis that is inclined rather than horizontal is a plunging fold. Plunging folds are called "plunging" because it looks like the folded bed plunges beneath the rock and soil around it.

This trial is a travesty. It's a travesty of a mockery of a sham of a mockery of a travesty of two mockeries of a sham.

– Woody Allen in *Bananas*

EXTRA MATTER

IF THE FOLD AXIS IS HORIZONTAL, THE FOLD IS NONPLUNGING. IF THE FOLD AXIS IS NOT HORIZONTAL, THE FOLD IS PLUNGING.

Superposition refers to the relative ages of layers of sediment. The deeper layers are older, and the top layers were deposited more recently. According to the principle of superposition, the youngest layer of rock should be on the top of a sedimentary sequence. This concept can get a little muddy, however, when the layers get folded.

Let's compare an anticline to a sub sandwich. (It may sound a little crazy, but bear with us.)

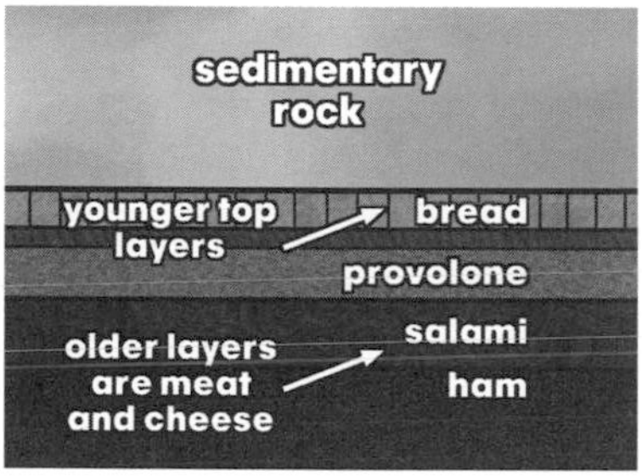

A sequence of sedimentary rock has the youngest layers on top and the oldest layers on the bottom. Now, pretend the older, bottom layers are meat and cheese, and the younger, top layers are bread.

Now pretend that the whole sedimentary unit gets pushed up into an anticline, so the youngest layers are on the top and sides of the anticline and the oldest layers are sandwiched in between. This sandwich is an upside-down sub sandwich, and the younger layers are like the sub roll—one unbroken piece of bread that cradles the older layers (the meat and cheese) on the inside.

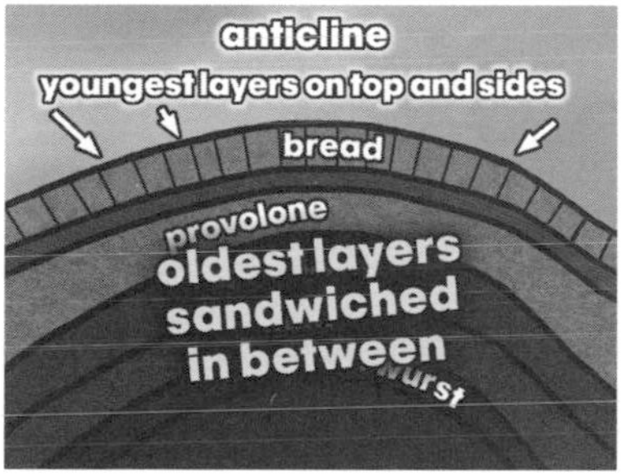

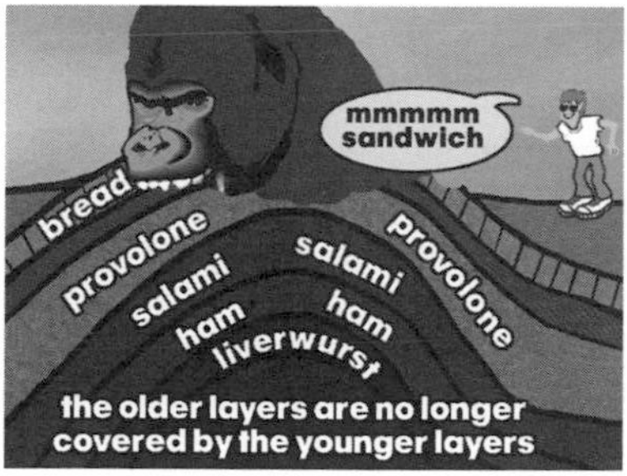

When the anticline has eroded to a flat surface, it will contain older rock in its center and younger rock on both sides of the center. Pretend the sub roll is sticking up out of the ground, and the meat and cheese are cradled inside the sub roll. The process of erosion comes along like a hungry giant and takes a few bites out of the part of the sub roll sticking up out of the ground.

The older layers (the meat and cheese) are no longer covered by the younger layer (the sub roll). The older layers are now exposed. If you looked at this sandwich poking up out of the ground, you would see a layer of bread (a younger layer) then some meat and cheese (the older layers that got exposed), then more bread, which is another younger layer.

0:31:47

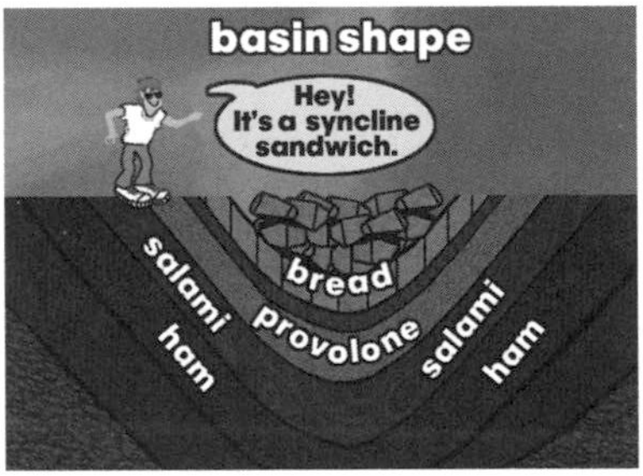

Now here's what happens when a syncline erodes on top. Remember, a syncline is shaped like a sink—it goes down in the middle and up on the sides—which is the opposite of the anticline. Refer back to the picture of the flattened sub sandwich with the meat and cheese on the bottom and the bread lying on the top. Now, look at this picture showing the middle pushed down and the sides pushed up.

We end up with an inside-out Martian sandwich. The meat and cheese, which are the older layers, are on the bottom and the outside. The bread, which represents the younger layers, are on the inside.

I'm just glad it'll be Clark Gable who's falling on his face and not Gary Cooper.

— Gary Cooper re. his decision not to take the leading role in *Gone with the Wind*

Quiz 10

1. What is the difference between stress and strain?

2. How do geologists represent a tilted rock on a geological map?

3. Name three ways a mountain can form.

4. Folds only form at the surface of the Earth. True or False?

5. What is orogenesis?

6. Can folds be formed by tensional forces (forces that pull the rock apart)?

7. What is the definition of a mountain? Why is it so vague?

QUIZ

8. Circle the correct terms:

An anticline is a (fold /fault) shaped somewhat like the letter (A/U/T/I) with the beds in the center being (younger /older) than the beds to either side.

9. What is the special term for the study of folds and faults?

HE HAD A LOVING FAMILY AND A TWIN SISTER (FRATERNAL, OF COURSE).
HE COULDN'T ASK FOR ANYTHING MORE.
EXCEPT PERHAPS ONE THING...

0:35:17

Section B: Fractures

I really admire your shoes... and as much as I'd like to have a pair just like them, I really wouldn't want to be in your shoes at this particular time and place.

– Steve Martin in *Roxanne*

Just like with legs and funny bones, we call it a fracture when rocks break in reaction to stress. Fractures represent a different reaction to stress than folds do. Rather than bending, some rocks just break apart. Rocks near the Earth's surface are especially likely to break when exposed to stress. Rocks that aren't deeply buried are more brittle, because they are not exposed to as much heat and pressure as the deeper rocks. Heat and pressure make rocks more malleable.

Rocks break more easily at weak spots such as tiny cracks. There are two types of fractures:

- **joints**
- **faults**

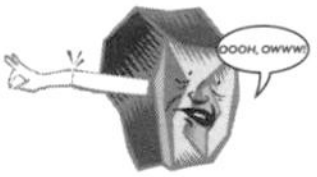

0:36:08

Joints are fractures along which no movement occurs. The rock is fractured, but the two separated parts of the rock do not move or scrape against each other.

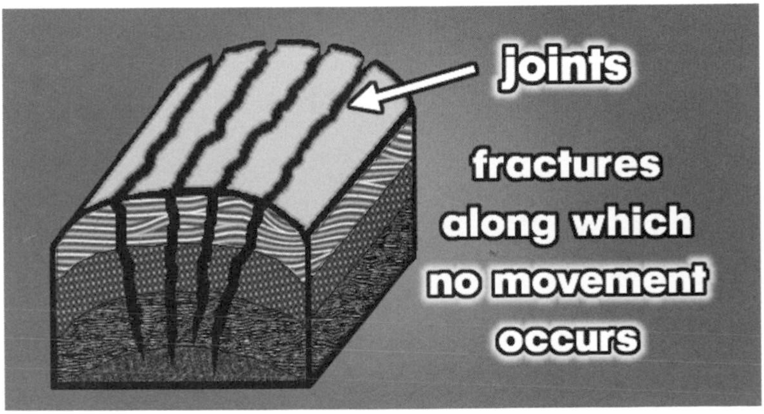

0:36:20

Faults are fractures in which the two separated sections of rock actually do move and scrape against each other. When one side of a fault moves considerably higher than the other, it can form a mountain. In this way, faulting contributes to mountain building.

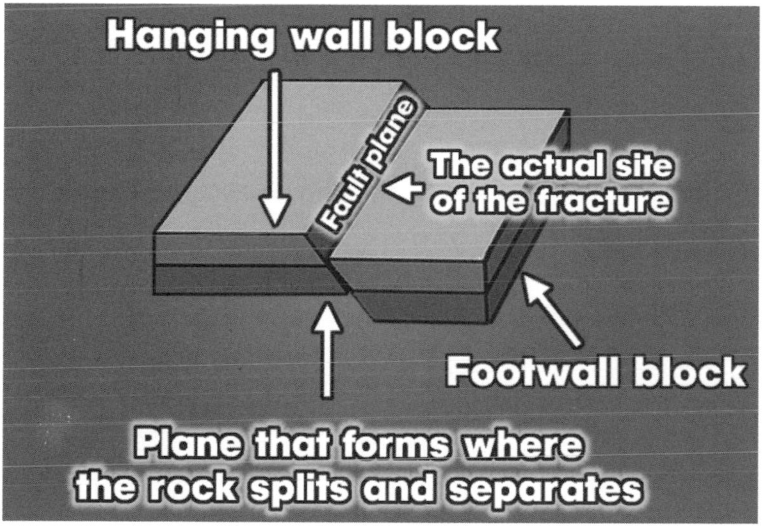
Hanging wall block
Fault plane
The actual site of the fracture
Footwall block
Plane that forms where the rock splits and separates

The **fault plane** is the actual site of the fracture. It is the plane that forms where the rock splits into two pieces.

The piece of the rock that lies under the fault plane is called the **footwall block**.

MORE CRUSTY STUFF:

THE FOOTWALL BLOCK IS UNDER THE FAULT PLANE, JUST LIKE YOUR FEET ARE UNDER YOU. THE HANGING WALL BLOCK IS HANGING OVER THE FAULT PLANE, JUST WHERE YOU HANG A LANTERN.

The terms strike and dip apply to faults, too. They are measurements that describe the orientation of the fault.

The piece of rock that lies on top of the fault plane is called the **hanging wall block**.

The strike of the fault plane is the direction of the line formed where the fault plane intersects with a horizontal surface. It's just like measuring the strike of a rock bed.

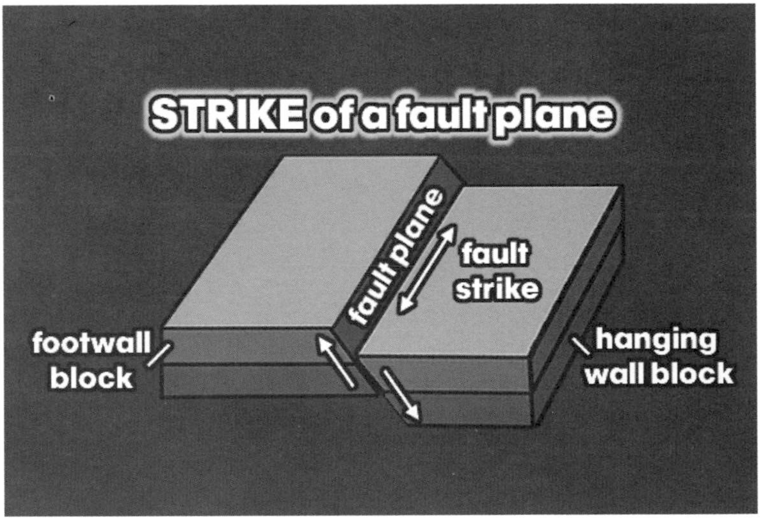

The dip is the measurement of the angle between the fault plane and a horizontal plane. We measure the dip of the fault the same way we measure the dip of an inclined rock bed. Again, the dip angle is measured from an imaginary line running perpendicular to the direction of the strike of the fault.

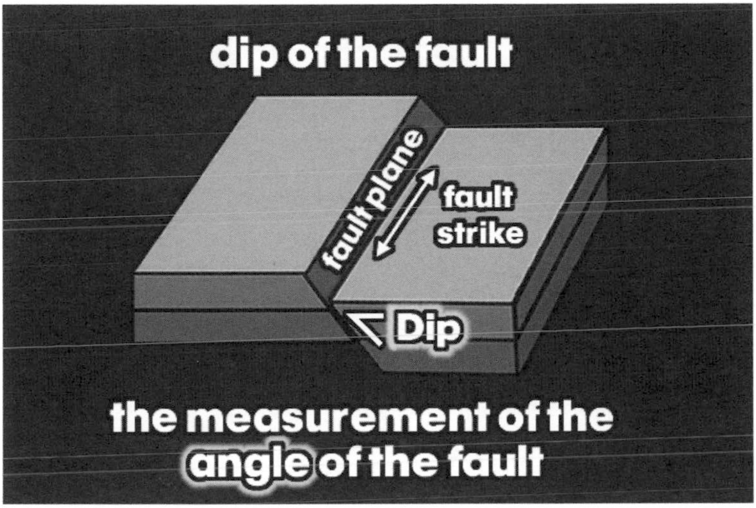

There are two categories of faults:

- **dip-slip faults**
- **strike-slip faults**

In a **dip-slip fault**, one side of the fault moves up or down relative to the other side. All movement of a dip-slip fault is parallel to the dip of the fault plane. In other words, the moving side will slide up or down parallel to the fault plane. If the fault plane is at an angle, the moving side will move up or down along the fault plane at that same angle.

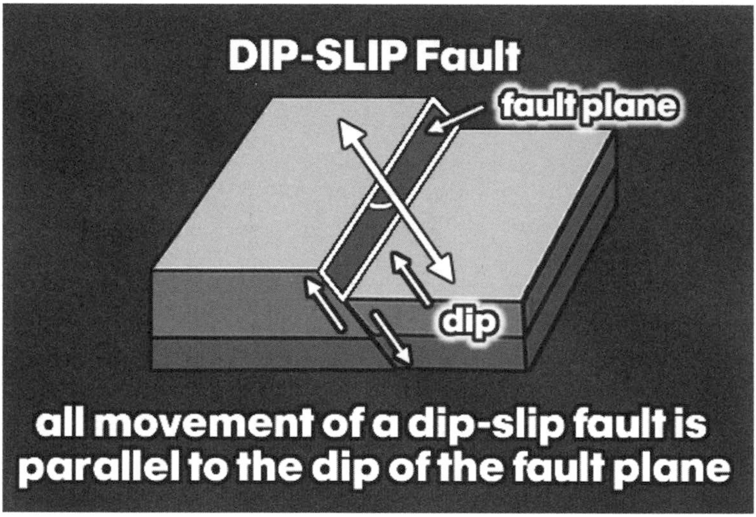
DIP-SLIP Fault
fault plane
dip
all movement of a dip-slip fault is parallel to the dip of the fault plane

In the diagram above, it looks like the hanging wall block (the side on top of the fault plane) slid downward relative to the footwall block (the side under the fault plane). Faults that have this type of movement are called normal faults. **Normal faults** are usually the result of the tension created by sections of rock moving away from each other.

Reverse
Normal

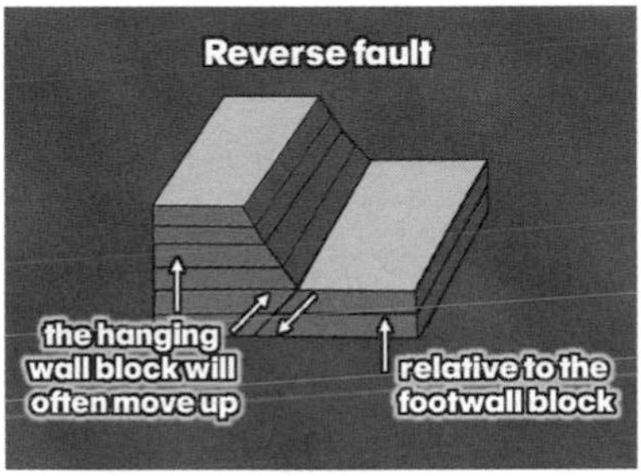
Reverse fault
the hanging wall block will often move up
relative to the footwall block

A **reverse fault** can occur when rocks are compressed. Under the stress of compression, the hanging wall block will often move upward relative to the footwall block, rather than downward as in the case of a normal fault. Dip-slip faults can be either normal or reverse faults, depending on whether the hanging wall block moves up or down in relation to the footwall block.

Cancel the kitchen scraps for lepers and orphans, no more merciful beheadings, and call off Christmas.

– Robin Hood: Prince of Thieves

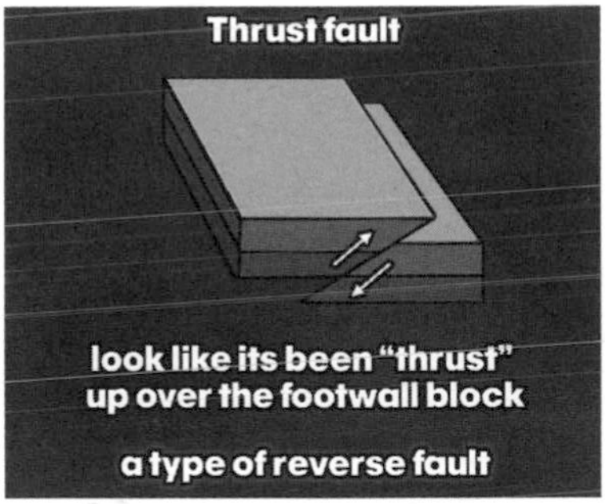
Thrust fault
look like its been "thrust" up over the footwall block
a type of reverse fault

A **thrust fault** is a type of reverse fault. The fault plane of a thrust fault lies at a low angle in relation to the horizontal plane. A thrust fault is really just a gently inclined reverse fault. The dip angle of a thrust fault is tight—less than 45 degrees. The hanging wall block looks like it has been thrust up over the footwall block.

EXTRA MATTER

Reverse and normal faults:

In a normal fault, the hanging wall block moves down in relation to the footwall block.

In a reverse fault, the hanging wall block moves up in relation to the footwall block.

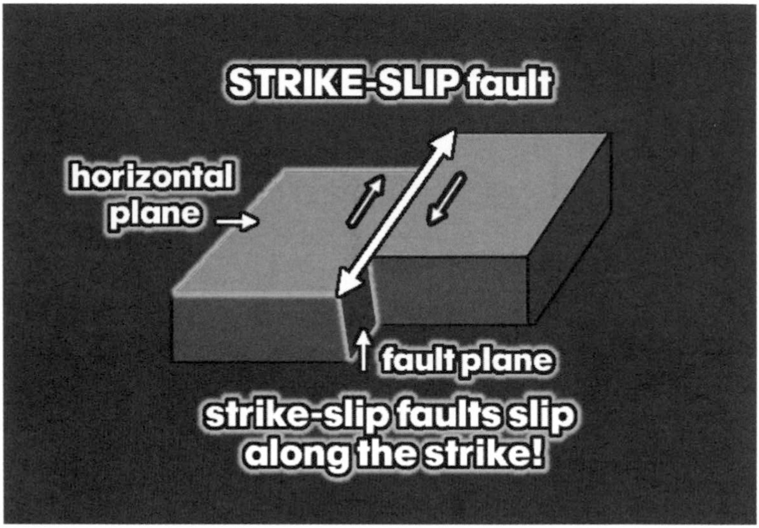

In a **strike-slip fault**, the sections of rock slide sideways past each other. This type of fault has lateral movement instead of vertical movement. All movement in a strike-slip fault is parallel to the fault plane's strike. The strike is the direction of the line formed where the fault plane meets a horizontal plane. The blocks on either side of a strike-slip fault move parallel to the line formed by the strike. In other words, *strike-slip faults slip along the strike*. (Try saying that one five times fast!)

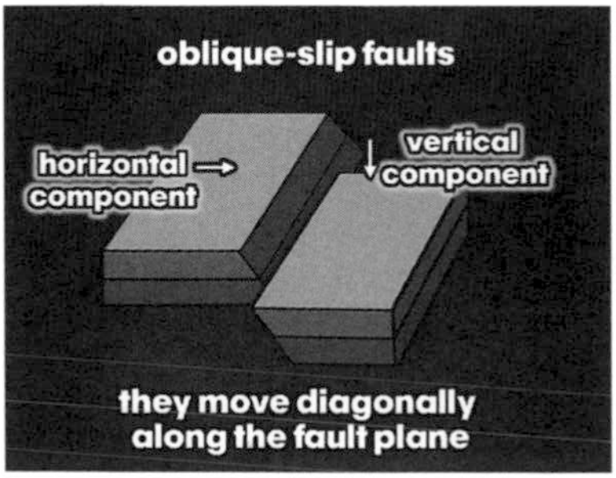

Oblique-slip faults combine the movement of dip-slip and strike-slip faults. Since they move diagonally along the fault plane, they have both a vertical and horizontal component.

Mountain Building

Mountains may form in several different ways:

- ▲ **Faulting:** The Tetons and the Rockies were formed mainly through faulting.
- ▲ **Erosion** around plutons: A mountain forms when the less-resistant rock around a giant pluton (batholith) erodes away, leaving a huge, erosion-resistant chunk sticking up out of the ground. The Sierra Nevadas in California and Nevada are exposed plutons.
- ▲ **Continental plate movement**: Continental plate movement causes magma to move upward toward the crust, forming plutons that can become mountains. Plate movement can also form mountains through volcanoes and faulting.

A really big, intense event that causes mountain building is an **orogeny**. When the tectonic plates crunch up against each other, huge sections of crust get pushed upward and form mountains. There are a couple of places on Earth where this form of mountain building is still going on.

WATCH WHERE YOU'RE GOING–PLATE FACE!

STUDY SIDEKICK

AS USUAL, YOUR INFORMATION STINKS.

– Telegram to *Time* magazine from Frank Sinatra

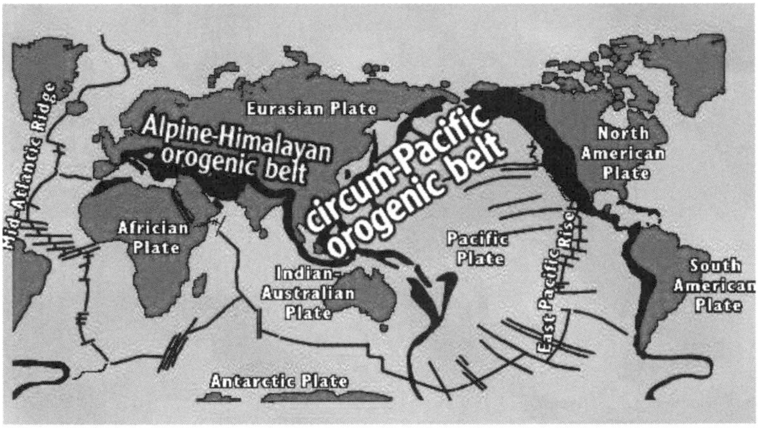

The Alpine-Himalayan orogenic belt and the circum-Pacific orogenic belt are currently undergoing mountain building. Plate movement causes serious deformation, but by and large, the movement is too slow for us to notice much change during our lifetime. Right now, India is moving northward at a rate of about 5 centimeters per year, but geologists estimate that between 40 and 50 million years ago, India was moving northward at about 10 to 15 centimeters per year. This amount of movement may seem almost insignificant, but it is responsible for the Himalayas.

VIDEO NOTES V2

SUMMARY

- ▲ When rocks break in reaction to stress, we call that break a fracture.
- ▲ There are two types of fractures:
  - ▲ joints: Fractures along which no movement occurs.
  - ▲ faults: Fractures in which the two separated sections of rock move and scrape against each other.
- ▲ The fault plane is the actual site of the fracture, where the rock splits and separates into two pieces.
- ▲ The piece of the rock that lies below the fault plane is the footwall block.
- ▲ The piece of the rock that lies above the fault plane is the hanging wall block.
- ▲ The fault plane's strike is the direction of the line formed where the fault plane intersects with a horizontal surface.
- ▲ The dip is the measurement of the angle between the fault plane and a horizontal plane perpendicular to the strike.
- ▲ In a dip-slip fault, one side of the fault moves upward or downward relative to the other side.

- In a strike-slip fault, the sections of rock slide sideways past each other.
- An oblique-slip fault moves diagonally, combining the horizontal and vertical components of the dip-slip and the strike-slip faults.
- When the hanging wall block moves downward in relation to the footwall block, the fault is a normal fault.
- When the hanging wall block moves upward in relation to the footwall block, the fault is a reverse fault.

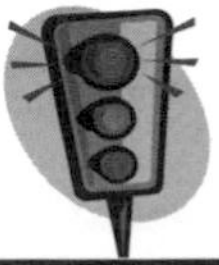

QUIZ

Quiz 11

1. Are faults formed by tensional or compressional forces?

2. What are the two categories of faults?

3. a. What two areas (belts) are experiencing orogenesis today?

   b. Circle the main process causing that orogenesis:

   folding / faulting / volcanism.

4. What kind of fault is the famous San Andreas fault? Where is it located?

5. What is the difference between a joint and a fault?

6. A geologist working close to Yellowstone Park finds evidence of tensional faulting. This tells her that no mountains could occur in this geological environment. True or False?

7. Normal faults are formed by (compressional/tensional) forces and the hanging wall moves (up/down) in relation to the foot wall.

8. Plutonic igneous rocks are (fine / coarse) grained, cool (underground / at the surface) and form (the Sierra Nevada Batholith of Nevada and California / the volcanic Cascade Range of Washington and Oregon).

9. On the diagram below, label the footwall and hanging wall blocks, show the relative direction of movement with arrows, and add a label stating what type of fault it is.

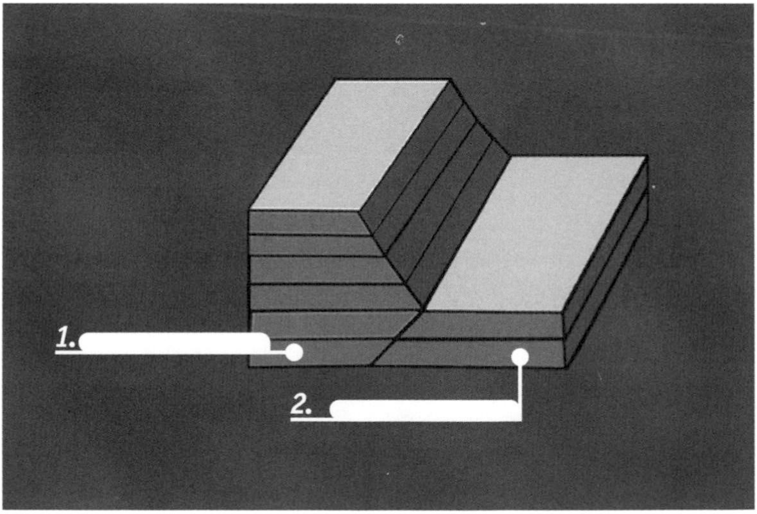

The Earth's Interior and Plate Tectonics

0:44:39

Section A: Seismology and the Earth's Interior

0:44:46

I'm your density.

– *Back to the Future*

When the Earth cuts loose some big release of energy such as movement along a fault, the whole Earth moves! This is called an earthquake.

0:44:50

According to the **elastic rebound** theory, rocks absorb stress the way a rubber band does. When rocks get stressed enough, they're likely to rupture quickly, like a rubber band breaks. The stress in the Earth pulls and pushes, and the rocks take all they can until they rupture. Then all hell breaks loose. The energy released from the rupture site moves outward in waves like ripples on the surface of a lake.

0:45:01

Earthquake Anatomy

0:45:22 The point within the Earth where the fault rupture starts is called the **focus** of the earthquake. The earthquake's energy emanates in all directions, originating at the focus. The **epicenter** of the quake is the point on the Earth's surface directly 0:45:33 above the focus.

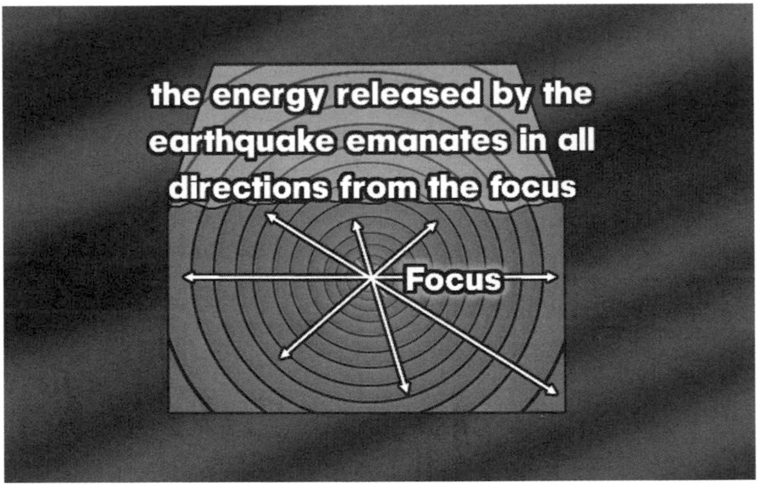

0:45:40 The energy waves released by the quake are called **seismic waves**. Seismic waves come in different types and sizes. Two different types of waves emitted by an earthquake are:

- **body waves:** travel through the Earth
- **surface waves:** ripple along the surface of the Earth

Seismographs record the **seismic waves** generated by earthquakes. Geologists monitor earthquakes by setting up seismograph stations at strategic points on the Earth. When an earthquake occurs, the waves travel through the Earth and are recorded by the seismograph.

AN EXTRA SHOVEL-FULL

THE FIRST KNOWN EARTHQUAKE DETECTOR WAS INVENTED SOME TIME BETWEEN THE FIRST AND SECOND CENTURIES C.E. BY THE CHINESE SCHOLAR CHANG HENG. THE DETECTOR WAS A VASE THAT SHOWED THE EFFECTS OF THE EARTHQUAKE'S SEISMIC WAVES BY A BALL FALLING OUT OF A DRAGON'S MOUTH INTO A FROG'S MOUTH BELOW.

We will discuss two types of **body waves**:

- **P-waves**, also known as **primary waves**
- **S-waves**, also known as **secondary waves**

The first body waves to arrive at a seismograph after an earthquake are the **P-waves** or primary waves. P-waves are body waves that can travel through solid rock, liquid, or gas within the Earth at a speed of about 6 to 14 kilometers per second, or 4 to 9 miles per second. These waves aren't fooling around. P-waves are also called compressional waves or push waves, because they expand and contract the material they're traveling through with a push-pull motion.

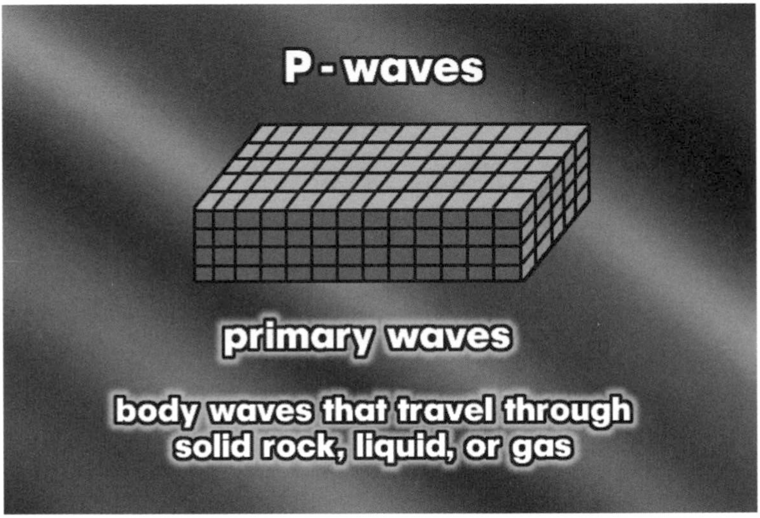

S-waves, or secondary waves, are the next body waves to shake up the seismograph. S-waves are slower than P-waves and can only travel through solid material. When they meet a liquid, they just basically conk out. S-waves are called shear waves because they cause the rock to vibrate at a right angle to the direction in which the wave is traveling. The vibration causes a sideways shaking motion. Liquids and gases can't support this shaking—which is why S-waves can't travel through liquid or gas. These waves generally travel at a speed of 4 to 7 kilometers per second.

EXTRA MATTER

THE S-WAVE IS LIKE THE "WAVE" THAT PEOPLE DO AT STADIUM SPORTING EVENTS. THE PEOPLE MOVE VERTICALLY UP AND DOWN, AND THE WAVE MOVES HORIZONTALLY.

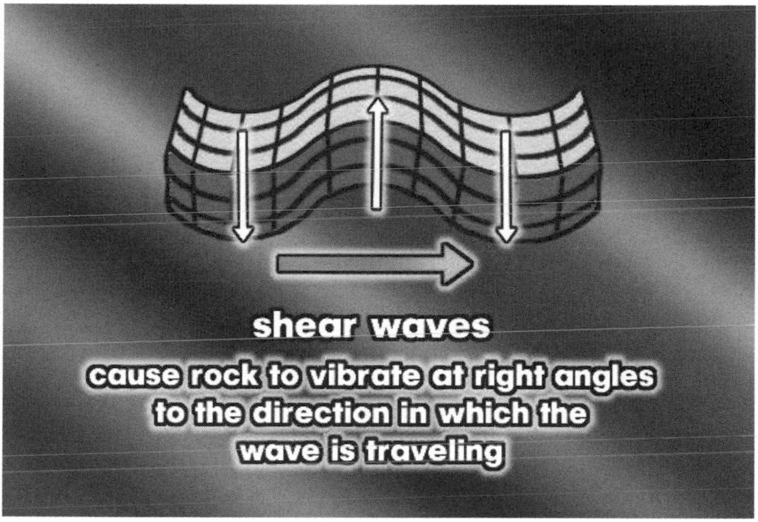

shear waves
cause rock to vibrate at right angles to the direction in which the wave is traveling

There are two important types of **surface waves**:

- **R-waves**, also known as **Rayleigh waves**
- **L-waves**, also known as **Love waves**

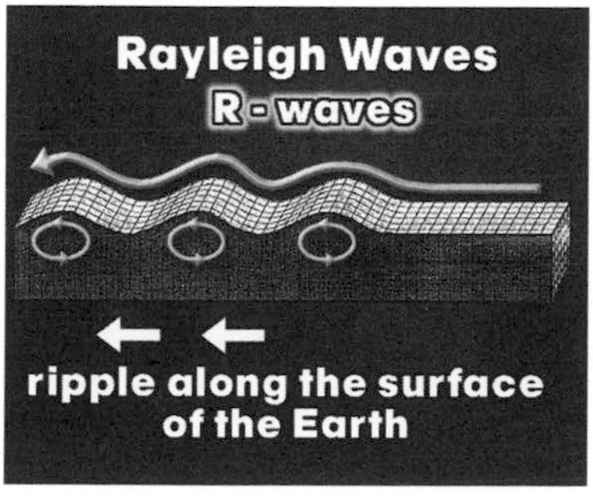

R-waves (Rayleigh waves), ripple along the surface of the Earth, rolling forward in an elliptical (oval-shaped) path, similar to the way ocean waves travel over the ocean's surface.

L-waves (Love waves), travel more quickly than R-waves. Love waves are not very loving at all—in fact, they're pretty freakin' destructive. As an L-wave moves forward, the ground it's traveling over moves horizontally from side to side in a sort of serpentine path.

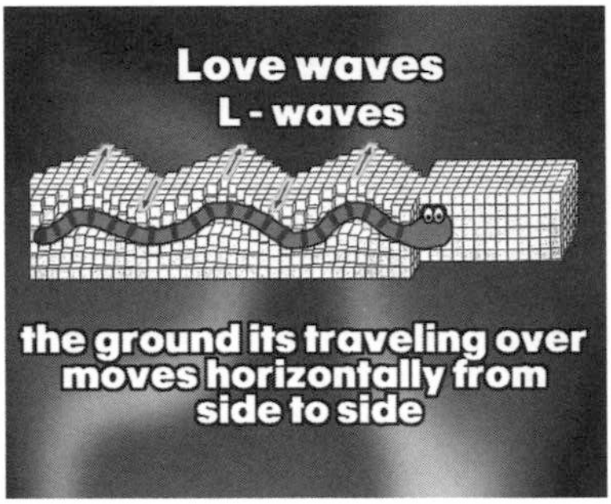

Seismologists use two measurements to indicate the strength of an earthquake:

- **magnitude**: the amount of energy the earthquake releases as measured by the **Richter magnitude scale**
- **intensity**: how much damage the quake causes in a particular location as measured by the **modified Mercalli scale**

0:48:48

The Richter magnitude scale measures the ground movement at a standard 100 kilometers from the earthquake's focus. Of course, it is rare to find a seismograph conveniently stationed 100 kilometers from the focus, so the amount of energy is calculated to allow for its distance from the focus. The amount of energy registered is called the earthquake's **magnitude**.

The Richter scale converts the intensity of seismic waves into a numerical value, using a base-10 logarithmic system. The scale starts at 1.0, the intensity at which a shake would cause the seismograph needle to move $\frac{1}{1000}$th of a millimeter at 100 kilometers from the focus. A magnitude of 2.0 makes the needle move 10 times as much, or $\frac{1}{100}$th of a millimeter.

Each consecutive number on the scale indicates an earthquake that releases about 30 times more energy than an earthquake ranking one number lower. The increase from one number to the next on the scale is exponential. For example, an earthquake that registers 5 on the Richter scale releases about 30 times more energy than an earthquake that registers 4, and it releases about 30 squared or 900 times more energy than an earthquake that registers 3. That's a lotta shakin'.

Technically, the Richter scale is open-ended, so the numbers can go up to infinity or down to negative infinity. The largest earthquake magnitude recorded is 8.6 on the Richter scale, and it's not likely there will ever be an earthquake that hits 9, because rocks are not strong enough to store the energy required to let loose anything that big. That whopping 8.6 occurred in Alaska in 1964.

Dinner is served promptly at eight in the private dining room. Those who are late do not get fruit cup.

– Mel Brooks in *High Anxiety*

Study Sidekick

AT THE OTHER END OF THE SCALE, VERY SMALL EARTHQUAKES CAN BE RECORDED IN AREAS WHERE THERE ARE MANY SEISMOGRAPHS AND SEISMOLOGISTS. MAGNITUDES AS SMALL AS 1 TO 2 ARE ROUTINELY RECORDED IN THE SAN FRANCISCO BAY AREA AND LOS ANGELES.

0:50:55 The modified **Mercalli scale** measures an earthquake's intensity by ranking the damage it does to people and property. Intensity varies from point to point depending on factors such as distance from the focus and the rock types present in the area. The Mercalli scale assigns numbers to the entire area affected by the quake. Areas that suffer less damage get a low Mercalli number, and areas that are severely wrecked get high numbers. High Mercalli numbers coincide roughly with the epicenter of the quake. Remember, the epicenter is the place on the Earth's surface right over the focus. This scale can help indicate which buildings and construction methods hold up best against earthquakes.

0:52:25 Seismographic records provide a lot of information about the Earth's interior. Tracking seismic waves from an earthquake's focus to various locations around the globe allows geologists to study how waves travel through the Earth, and gives an indication about the structure and composition of the Earth's **core**. Geologists found that some P-waves that passed through the Earth's core arrived at the other side much more slowly than they had predicted, and some never even arrived at all. What's more, they found that the S-waves were completely blocked by the core. Knowing that, can you guess what seismic waves taught geologists about the Earth's interior? Go ahead. Take a guess. C'mon. Take a guess.

If you said, "It means that part of the Earth's core might be liquid," then you win an all-expenses-paid cruise to the beautiful Carribean!

Ha. Fat chance.

Anyway, the P-waves, on the other hand, aren't completely blocked at the core, but they lose energy and get deflected at a depth of 2,900 kilometers (1,800 miles). This is the depth of the core-mantle boundary, where the layer of the Earth called the **mantle** ends, and the layer called the **outer core** begins. P-waves don't travel as fast through the core as they do through the mantle, so P-waves are another indication that the core has a different composition from the mantle.

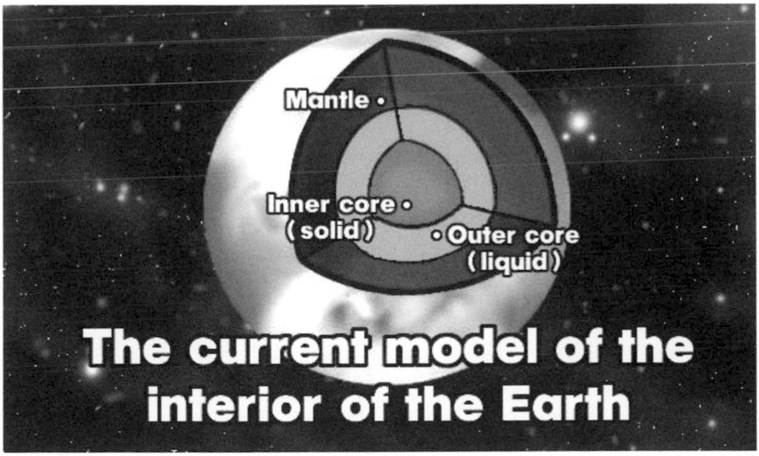

Geologists believe the **inner core**, which is the innermost part of the Earth, is a solid ball that consists mostly of iron and perhaps some nickel, which together form an iron-nickel alloy. The **outer core** is the part of the Earth that scientists think is liquid. It consists largely of iron, but it may also have some sulfur, maybe some silicon, and possibly some small amounts of nickel and potassium. Scientists believe that the inner core may have also been liquid, but it has cooled and crystallized.

Geologists believe that the mantle has roughly the same composition throughout, but its structural state varies at different depths. The bulk composition of the mantle is mafic (silicate minerals rich in iron and magnesium). We give names to the various zones within the mantle:

> **WE ALSO RECOGNIZE THE TRANSITION ZONE, WHICH LIES WITHIN THE UPPER MANTLE. THIS AREA BORDERS THE LOWER MANTLE, WHERE A DRAMATIC INCREASE IN DENSITY OCCURS AND SEISMIC WAVE VELOCITY INCREASES.**

- **lower mantle**
- **upper mantle**
- **asthenosphere (within the upper mantle)**

There is a special layer in the upper mantle called the **asthenosphere,** approximately 60 to 250 kilometers below the Earth's surface. Seismic waves slow down considerably at the depth of the asthenosphere. That's because the rocks in the asthenosphere are close to their melting point, so they are more pliable.

Seismic waves cruise through the upper mantle at a faster rate than through the crust. The boundary that separates the upper mantle from the crust is called the **Mohorovicic discontinuity**, or just the "Moho," and is defined by a sharp increase in the velocity of P-waves. The crust, the Moho, and the part of the upper mantle above the asthenosphere constitute a brittle set of layers called the lithosphere.

Don't let that little frankfurter run your life.

— Bruce Jay Friedman

Check out This Other Important Stuff:

1. The interior of the earth. See **OTHER IMPORTANT STUFF 9**, page 237.
2. Seismic waves. See **OTHER IMPORTANT STUFF 9**, page 237.

Quiz 12

1. List the various shells or parts of the Earth in order, moving outward from the center of the Earth.

2. Name two reasons geologists think the outer core is liquid.

3. A geologist is hoping to estimate earthquake intensity during the Paleozoic Era. He is going to use the modified Mercalli scale. Is he using the correct scale? Why or why not?

4. Which seismic waves arrive first during an earthquake? Describe the movement of these waves.

5. What separates the crust from the upper mantle?

6. Name and describe the two types of surface seismic waves.

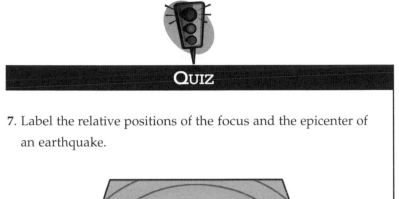

7. Label the relative positions of the focus and the epicenter of an earthquake.

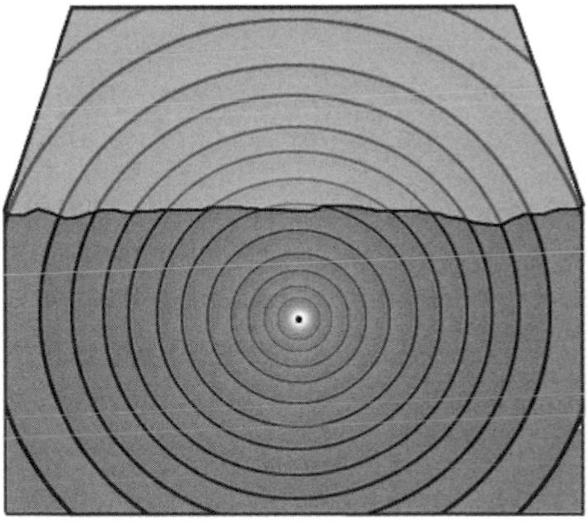

8. Will there ever be an earthquake of 9 on the Richter scale?

9. Geologists expect that one day they will be able to sample the rocks of the Earth's core to find out if they are really iron and nickel. True or False?

0:56:05 # Section B: Plate Tectonics

We've already introduced the idea of continental plates and how they move and bump into each other to cause volcanoes and earthquakes and potentially deadly stuff like that. This is because plates are rude by nature. They make no effort whatsoever to accommodate each other. Let's go into more detail now about the **plate tectonic theory**.

0:56:32 In 1915, the German meteorologist Alfred Wegner developed the idea that all the continents were once joined in a single, giant landmass that broke apart, allowing the continents to drift away from each other. This large-scale movement of the continents was called continental drift.

0:56:55 Wegner proposed that a supercontinent once contained all of Earth's landmasses joined together in one giant hunk of land. He called the supercontinent **Pangea**, meaning "all land." The way the South American and African continents clearly fit together, along with the remarkable similarity of rocks, geologic structures, and fossils on opposite sides of the Atlantic provided Wegner with enough evidence to get the attention of the scientific community. Many experts vehemently opposed Wegner's hypothesis anyway and dismissed his theory.

MORE CRUSTY STUFF:

HERE ARE THE MAIN REASONS WEGNER'S THEORY WAS NOT ACCEPTED:

1. **LACK OF A FEASIBLE MECHANISM TO DRIVE THE PLATE MOTION. WEGNER LIKENED MOON TIDES TO OCEAN TIDES TO EXPLAIN THE MOVEMENT.**
2. **NO ONE COULD EXPLAIN WHY THE OCEANIC CRUST REMAINED IN PLACE WHILE THE CONTINENTS MOVED THROUGH IT LIKE HUGE ICEBREAKERS.**

The idea of continental drift was revived in the 1950's and evolved into the theory of plate tectonics. All the data Wegner collected is still accounted for in this new theory. The difference is that now we have identified the mechanism that moves the plates.

Geologists continue to study continental plates, and modern science generally accepts the theory of plate tectonics. In fact, plate tectonics revolutionized the science of geology. The theory provides a framework for understanding earthquakes, volcanoes, mountain ranges, rock types, and ore deposits in our dynamic planet.

In the theory of plate tectonics, the lithosphere (which consists of part of the mantle and the crust) is subdivided into about a dozen major lithospheric plates. These plates can slide around on the asthenosphere in distinct units until they break or buckle at their boundaries. The rocks in the asthenosphere are not brittle and hard like the rocks in the lithosphere. The hot, sometimes flowing rock of the asthenosphere provides a skating rink of sorts for the lithospheric plates.

What the heck kind of force would it take to move a continent? In the 1950's, Harry Hess of Princeton University came up with
0:59:18 a notion: the theory of **sea-floor spreading**.

Volcanic ridges in the ocean erupt frequently. There's an especially large volcanic ridge called the Mid-Atlantic Ridge which runs right down the middle of the Atlantic Ocean. As these undersea volcanoes cough up new lava, they form new crust, or new sea floor, which shoves the older sea floor sideways. This force is persistent and formidable enough to move continents.

As the plates slide around, they can move away from each other, bump into each other, or slide past each other. Naturally, there are special terms for these plate interactions. A **plate**
1:00:01 **boundary** is a division between two plates. There are three distinct types of plate boundaries:

- **divergent boundaries**
- **convergent boundaries**
- **transform boundaries**

Divergent boundaries occur where plates move away from each other. At the Mid-Atlantic Ridge, where the volcanic action causes sea-floor spreading, the plates on either side of the ridge are moving away from each other, so the boundary between the plates is divergent.

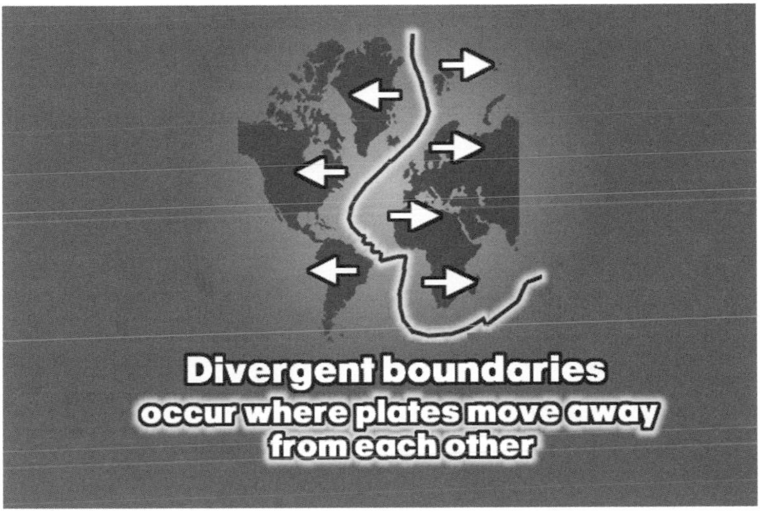
Divergent boundaries
occur where plates move away from each other

We don't like their sound, and guitar music is on the way out.

— Decca Recording Co. rejecting the Beatles, 1962

Convergent boundaries occur where plates collide. Right now plates are colliding and high mountains are forming at the convergent boundary between India and Eurasia, because neither of the two plates is willing to move.

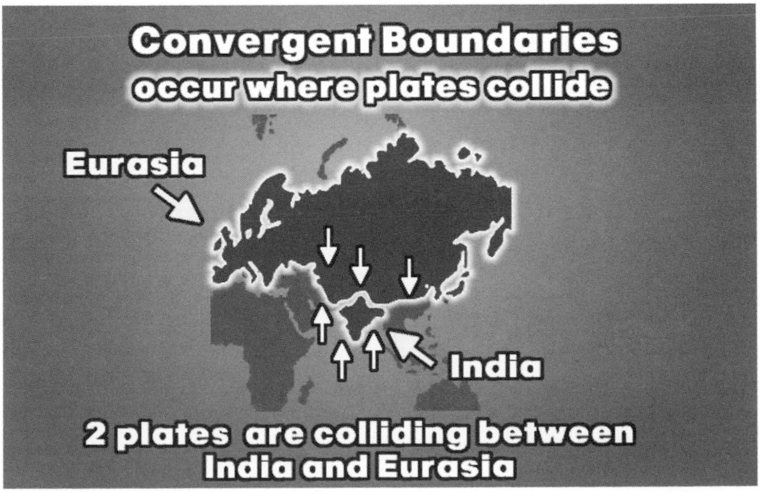
Convergent Boundaries
occur where plates collide
Eurasia
India
2 plates are colliding between India and Eurasia

STUDY SIDEKICK

Here we have the two ships that pass in the night: **transform boundaries** occur at transform faults, where the plates slide sideways past each other in opposite directions. The San Andreas fault is a famous transform fault that runs through California, separating the North American Plate from the Pacific Plate.

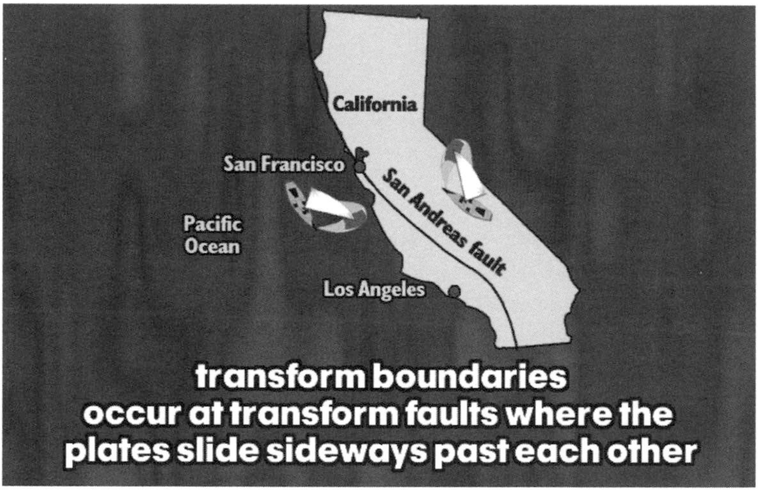

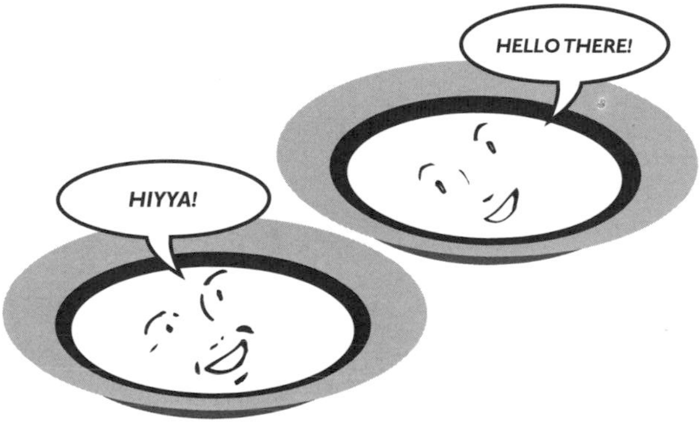

VIDEO NOTES

V2

SUMMARY

- In 1915, Alfred Wegner proposed that all the continents were once joined in a giant landmass called Pangea.
- According to Wegner's theory, Pangea broke apart and the continents moved away from each other through a process called continental drift.
- Scientists believe the lithosphere is currently subdivided into about a dozen lithospheric plates that slide around on the hot, pliable asthenosphere.
- According to a theory proposed by Harry Hess, the continents move in a process called sea-floor spreading. In sea-floor spreading, erupting volcanic ridges on the ocean floor form new crust moving outward from the ridge persistently enough to push continents.
- The continental plates can move toward or away from each other at their boundaries.
- At divergent boundaries, plates move away from each other.
- At convergent boundaries, plates move toward each other.
- At transform boundaries, plates slide sideways past each other.

Quiz 13

Everything that can be invented has been invented.

— Charles H. Duell, Commissioner, U.S. Office of Patents, 1899

1. Tectonic plates are composed of which two parts of the Earth?

2. The theory of plate tectonics is a neat theory, but geologists don't use it much. True or False?

3. The lithosphere moves on the (core / crust / asthenosphere) which is (brittle/ cold/ pliable).

4. The crust being created at (convergent / divergent / transform) plate boundaries is (oceanic / continental) crust and is (felsic / intermediate / mafic) in composition.

5. What is the driving force of plate movement?

6. What are the two main differences between the continental drift theory and the plate tectonic theory?

7. What is the name given to the land when all the continents were joined together?

QUIZ

8. The jigsaw fit of South America and Africa is purely coincidental. True or False?

9. Seismic S-waves stop in the asthenosphere. True or False?

10. Name a classic location for a divergent, a convergent, and a transform plate margin.

1:02:45

Earth Surface Processes

1:02:52

Section A: River Systems

Mother nature was into recycling long before we humans got into it. Water is recycled all the time from the oceans to the atmosphere, from the atmosphere to the land, and then from the land back to the oceans. This process is called the

1:02:55 **hydrologic cycle**.

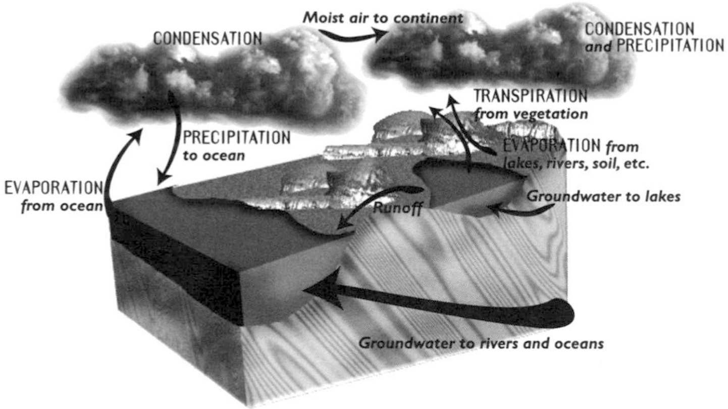

Energy from the sun drives the hydrologic cycle. Water evaporates easily as the sun's rays hit the surface of the Earth.

- ▲ 85% of the water entering the atmosphere from evaporation comes from the oceans.
- ▲ The remaining 15% evaporates from the land.

Once water vapor is in the atmosphere, it condenses into clouds, and then rains or snows back down onto the Earth.

- ▲ About 80% of **precipitation** falls right back into the oceans.
- ▲ The remaining 20% falls on the land.

The water on land makes its way back into the oceans through a process called **runoff**. Rivers and streams participate in the runoff process by returning the water to the oceans. 1:03:42

Let's talk about **rivers** and **streams**, starting with some terms that describe the way water moves over land. We'll use the word "stream" to refer to any flowing water in a **channel**.

1. **Velocity** is simply how fast water is flowing downstream. A stream's velocity is influenced by several factors:

   - ▲ the **gradient** of the channel (the steeper the slope the stream flows down, the greater the stream's velocity.)
   - ▲ the shape of the channel
   - ▲ the size of the channel
   - ▲ the depth of the channel
   - ▲ the roughness of the channel

2. **Discharge** refers to the amount of water that flows past a certain point in the stream in a certain amount of time.

1:04:38

3. **Competence** is the stream's ability to carry material of a given size in its current. Naturally, the faster the current, the larger the particles the stream can carry. Streams can transport material in three ways:

1:04:56

- ▲ **dissolved load**, or material (ions) that has dissolved into the stream water from chemical weathering
- ▲ **suspended load**, or little particles, like clay and silt, that ride along in the current
- ▲ **bed load**, or larger material like sand and gravel that travel along the bottom of the channel.

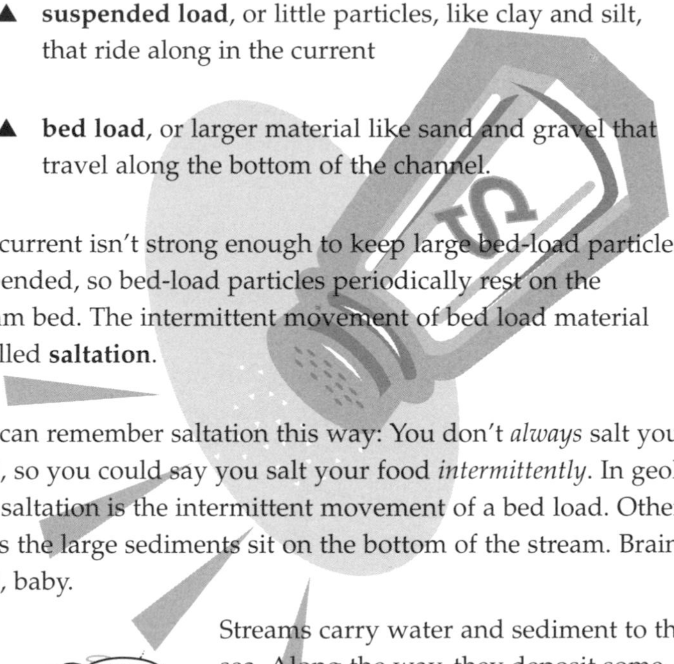

The current isn't strong enough to keep large bed-load particles suspended, so bed-load particles periodically rest on the stream bed. The intermittent movement of bed load material is called **saltation**.

You can remember saltation this way: You don't *always* salt your food, so you could say you salt your food *intermittently*. In geology, saltation is the intermittent movement of a bed load. Other times the large sediments sit on the bottom of the stream. Brain food, baby.

Streams carry water and sediment to the sea. Along the way, they deposit some of the sediment they carry in the channel of the stream. Channel deposits, called **bars**, are usually composed of sand and gravel. The sand and gravel will likely be picked up again and transported further downstream.

Streams that carry a lot of sediment can build up so many bars in the channel that the water gets routed through the network of little channels. The little channels cross each other and weave a pattern, which is why this type of stream is called a braided stream.

Nature's got a hankering after experiments.

— Tom Robbins, *Even Cowgirls Get the Blues*

1:07:01

large deposites tend to form where streams meet big bodies of water
Deltas
beds of sediment that are shaped like a triangle

Streams start to lose velocity just before they dump into a lake or an ocean. The larger body of slower-moving water is like a barrier that slows the quicker stream water and causes the sediment to be deposited in the channel. These large deposits are called **deltas**. A delta is a triangle-shaped bed of sediment whose point faces upstream and whose wide end leads into the lake or ocean.

Delta sediment forms a triangular bed with three distinct layers:

▲ **Bottomset bed**: consists of fine sediments carried the farthest and then settle out to form an under-lying bed.

▲ **Foreset bed**: made of sand and silt; slopes gently down from the stream towards the larger body of water.

▲ **Topset bed**: consists of the coarsest or largest sediment particles—sand.

The three layers lie in vertical sequence, one layer on top of another.

As the stream moves through the coarser topset beds, the main channel separates into several smaller channels called **distributaries**. The term distributary is easy to remember, because distributaries distribute water away from a main channel into smaller channels.

A **tributary** is a smaller channel of water that feeds into a larger body of water. It pays tribute to the larger body.

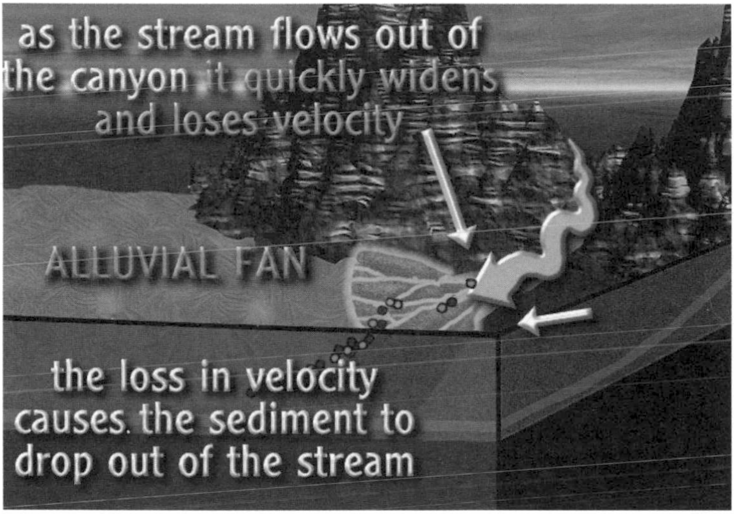
as the stream flows out of the canyon it quickly widens and loses velocity
ALLUVIAL FAN
the loss in velocity causes the sediment to drop out of the stream

1:08:52

Alluvial fans are similar to deltas, but they develop in different areas and for slightly different reasons. When a stream full of sediment flows through a narrow mountain canyon, it runs fast and deep. As the stream flows out of the canyon and is no longer confined by the mountains, it widens quickly and loses velocity. The loss in velocity causes the sediment to drop out of the stream into the bottom of the channel, forming large deposits. These fan-shaped deposits are called alluvial fans.

I had a wonderful evening. But it wasn't this one.

— Groucho Marx

1:09:23

Meandering streams are single-channel streams that flow in a serpentine pattern. Each looping curve of the stream is called a **meander**.

When the stream bypasses one of the meanders and alters its channel by flowing straight to its next curve, the new, straight part of the channel is called a **cutoff**. The abandoned bend becomes a little crescent-shaped body of water called an

1:09:33

oxbow lake. Eventually, the oxbow lake will fill up with sediment and turn into what is called an **oxbow scar** that lies beside the stream channel.

Streams and their tributaries drain the water on the surface of the Earth. They are components of **drainage systems** which directly or indirectly carry the surface water and **groundwater** from the land to the oceans. Groundwater is the water stored

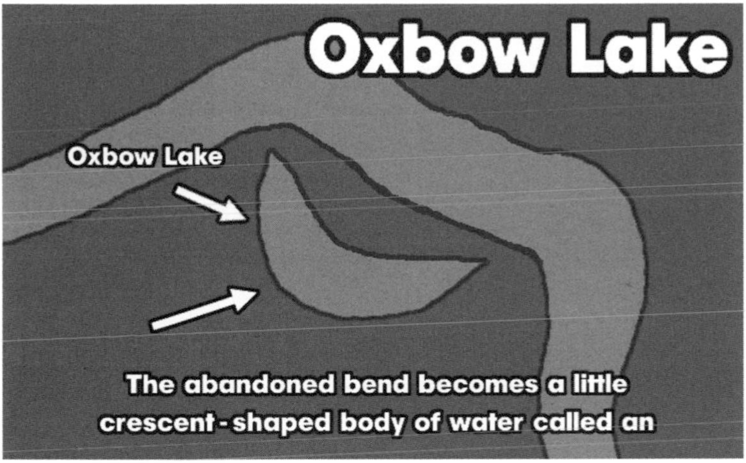
Oxbow Lake
Oxbow Lake
The abandoned bend becomes a little
crescent-shaped body of water called an

underground in the open pore spaces in unconsolidated sediment, soil, or between mineral grains in a rock. Groundwater may also be stored in larger open spaces such as fractures.

A **drainage basin** is a specific area of land served by its own drainage system. Drainage basins can vary tremendously in size. For example, the Colorado River Drainage Basin covers 243,000 square miles. All the streams that drain the entire area interconnect to form one giant drainage system. Within that major drainage system is a series of smaller drainage systems associated with the Colorado River's tributaries. The White Oak Run Drainage Basin in the Shenandoah National Park in Virginia is only 14 square miles, but it is part of the much larger drainage basin of the Shenandoah River. Despite differences in size, all drainage systems drain water from the area they serve and directly or indirectly carry it to the ocean.

1:09:55

EXTRA MATTER

DRAINAGE DIVIDES ARE ELEVATED AREAS OF LAND THAT SEPARATE DRAINAGE BASINS FROM ONE AN OTHER. THE GREAT DIVIDE OR CONTINENTAL DIVIDE SEPARATES THE DRAINAGE OF NORTH AMERICA WEST INTO THE PACIFIC OCEAN AND EAST INTO THE ATLANTIC OCEAN.

1:10:05

There are four common types of drainage systems, and each type represents a different pattern of networking streams:

- **dendritic drainage systems**
- **rectangular drainage systems**
- **trellis drainage systems**
- **radial drainage systems**

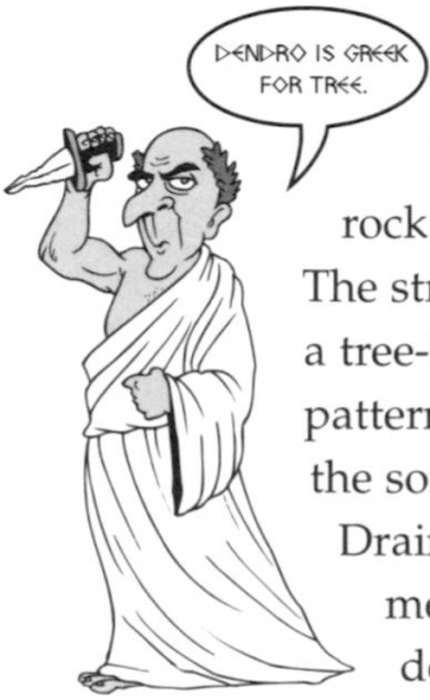
DENDRO IS GREEK FOR TREE.

Dendritic drainage occurs in drainage basins with gentle slopes, where all the rock and soil erodes at about the same rate. The streams merge into more major streams in a tree-like branching pattern. This stream pattern is influenced by the rock underlying the soil in the drainage basin, called the bedrock. Drainage basins located on gently tilting sedimentary rock tend to have dendritic drainage systems.

Dendritic Drainage
Gentle slopes where all the rock and soil erode at about the same rate

If the Phone Doesn't Ring, It's Me.

– Song title by Jimmy Buffet

Rectangular drainage basins sit on bedrock criss-crossed in a rectangular pattern by a series of joints and faults. The streams follow the joints and faults, so they also intersect each other at right angles and form a rectangular pattern.

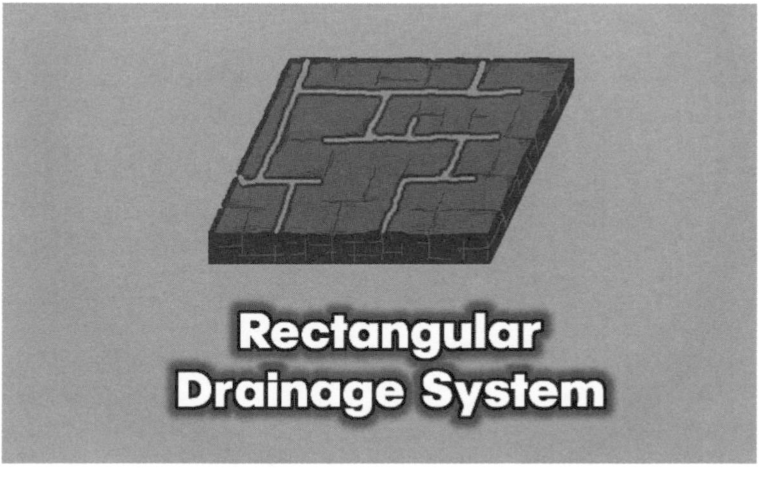
Rectangular Drainage System

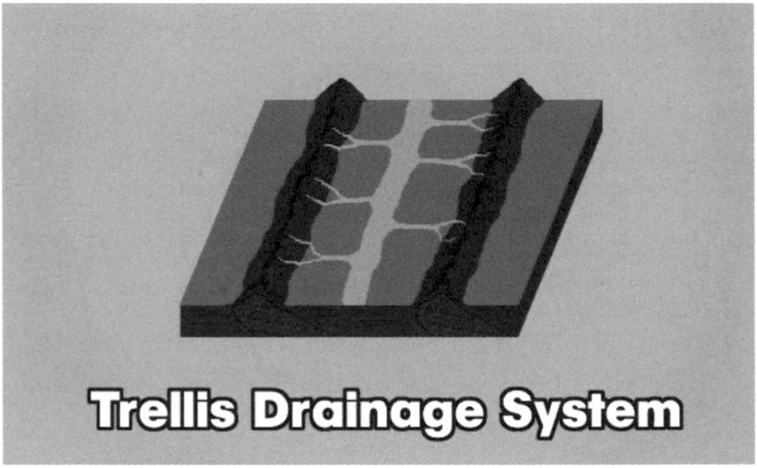

Trellis drainage systems are common in the drainage basins of Virginia, Pennsylvania, and other parts of the eastern U.S. where rocks, folded into anticlines and synclines, alternate with valleys. In a trellis drainage system, a stream runs down a valley between two mountains, and smaller streams flow down the mountains to join the valley stream at nearly right angles.

A radial drainage system's streams flow outward from a central upland area.

1:12:28

Drainage patterns can change over time. Streams actually get longer as runoff entering the stream erodes the land near the head of the stream. This process is called **headward erosion**.

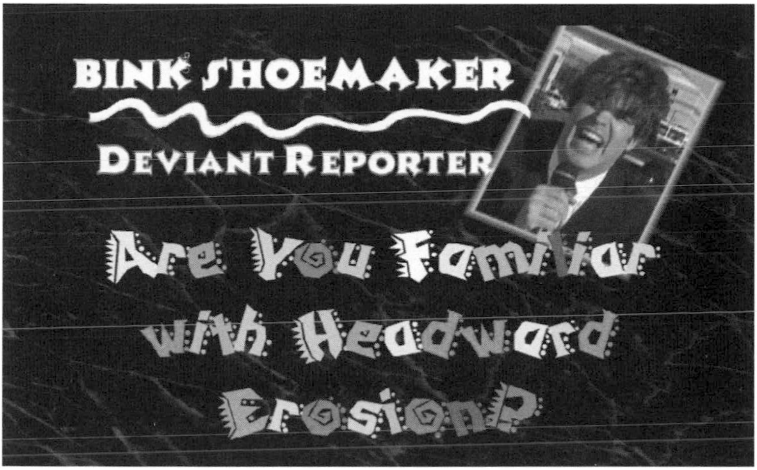

BINK SHOEMAKER
DEVIANT REPORTER
Are You Familiar with Headward Erosion?

Here's the deal with headward erosion: Let's say a stream begins halfway up a hill. If the ground uphill from the stream erodes and forms a channel and water flows down that channel and joins the stream, the new channel eventually just becomes part of the stream. Now the stream starts closer to the top of the hill, actually making the stream longer.

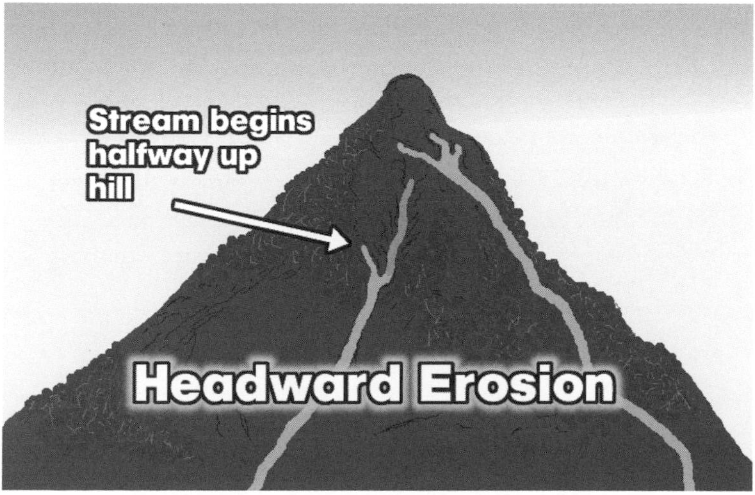

1:13:09

If headward erosion moves the head of a stream back far enough, the lengthening stream may back right into another stream. When this happens, the stream experiencing headward erosion will cut into the flow of the other stream, diverting the other stream's water into its own channel. This sneaky fluvial maneuver is called **stream piracy**.

You may have noticed that sometimes a stream cuts right through mountain ridges. Did you ever wonder how the stream made its path through the ridge? It seems that the water would have to defy gravity to go over the ridge before eroding a level channel.

Well, obviously the stream never defies gravity. The stream makes its path through the ridge by a process called **superposition**. Superposition is the reason the Potomac River cuts through Appalachian mountain ridges. 1:13:36

WE USED THE TERM "SUPERPOSITION" EARLIER IN REFERENCE TO SEDIMENTARY ROCKS. YOU REMEMBER--IT'S THE PRINCIPLE THAT IN A SEDIMENTARY SEQUENCE, THE YOUNGER LAYERS ARE ON TOP AND THE OLDER LAYERS ARE ON THE BOTTOM. NOW WE'RE TALKING ABOUT A DIFFERENT TYPE OF SUPERPOSITION, WHICH IS SOMETIMES CALLED SUPERIMPOSITION. DON'T GET 'EM MIXED UP!

During the Mesozoic Era, 245 to 66 million years ago, the Appalachian mountain region was a flat, eroded plain. Several streams, including the stream we now call the Potomac River, flowed eastward across the plain toward the Atlantic Ocean. During the beginning of the Cenozoic Era, about 66 million years ago, the Appalachian area experienced regional uplift and erosion which formed the present-day Appalachian Mountains. Instead of diverting its course around the uplifting mountains, the Potomac maintained its well-established path, eroding the rock that rose up in its path and forming a gap for itself called a water gap.

Stream Valleys

Valleys usually have streams flowing through them. Often, the stream is responsible for forming the valley. When streams erode the rock and soil beneath them, it's called **downcutting**.
1:15:06 Downcutting only occurs when the stream isn't carrying a big sediment load and has excess energy. The excess energy cuts the valley beneath the stream. If downcutting were the only force involved in valley formation and the stream just kept cutting straight downward, all valleys would be steep-sided, like canyons. That doesn't happen, though, because there are many forces involved in valley formation, including the process of **lateral erosion**.

1:15:32

Lateral erosion occurs when the stream cuts into the lower parts of the valley walls on either side of it, destabilizing the walls so they crumble down toward the stream. Mass wasting, the tendency of rocks and stuff to move downhill under the force of gravity, also contributes to the formation of valleys with sloping sides. The result is a **V-shaped valley**, which is the typical cross-sectional shape of a stream-cut valley.

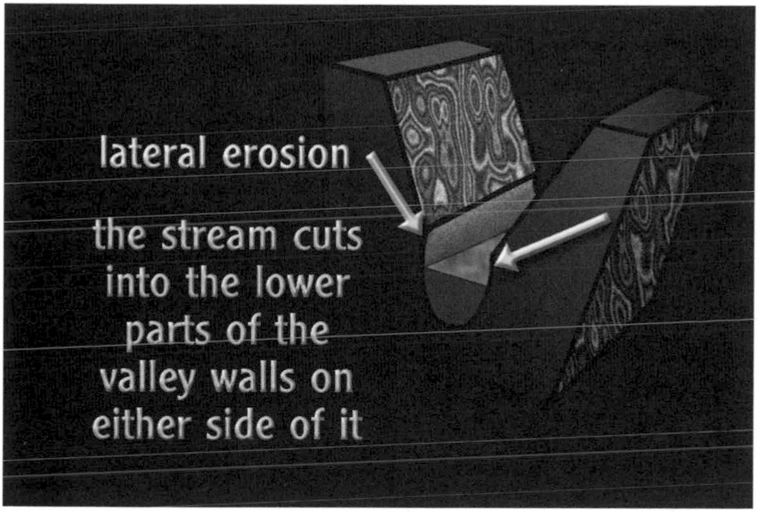
lateral erosion
the stream cuts into the lower parts of the valley walls on either side of it

Check out This Other Important Stuff:

1. Other channel factors related to velocity. See **OTHER IMPORTANT STUFF 10**, page 239.

2. Graded streams and base level. See **OTHER IMPORTANT STUFF 10**, page 239.

Quiz 14

1. Name and describe the three types of load a river carries.

2. A stream not only erodes rock and sediment, it also deposits sediment. True or False?

3. Draw the dendric drainage system.

4. How can a stream increase its length?

5. What is a stream?

Quiz

6. A stream valley is typically U/ V/ W / X shaped.

7. Explain how an oxbow lake is formed.

8. All drainage basins are the same size. True or False?

9. What is a distributary and how is it different from a tributary?

10. Fill in the blanks to complete the hydrologic cycle.

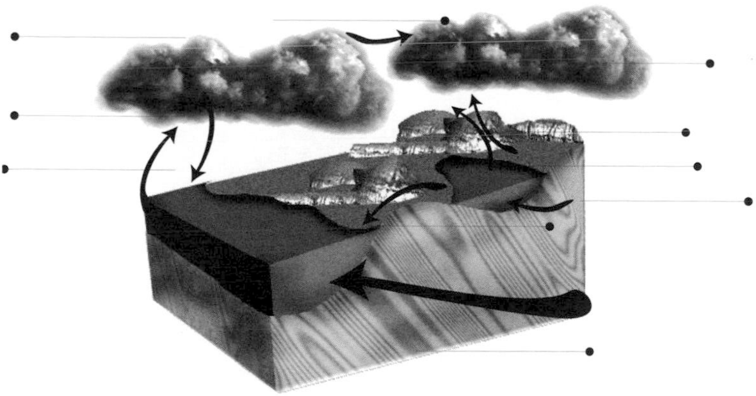

Get me Ham on five, hold the Mayo.

– Airplane

1:16:46

Section B: Shoreline Systems

1:16:51

Shorelines are areas where water meets land and humans walk around in skimpy clothing. Shorelines extend from the point where the water gets lowest at low tide to the point where the waves lap the highest during a storm.

1:17:05

Most **waves** are created by wind blowing over water, transferring energy from the moving air to the water. Waves get bigger (gnarlier) if the wind blows harder, blows for a long time, or blows over a larger area of water.

Here's the anatomy of a wave.

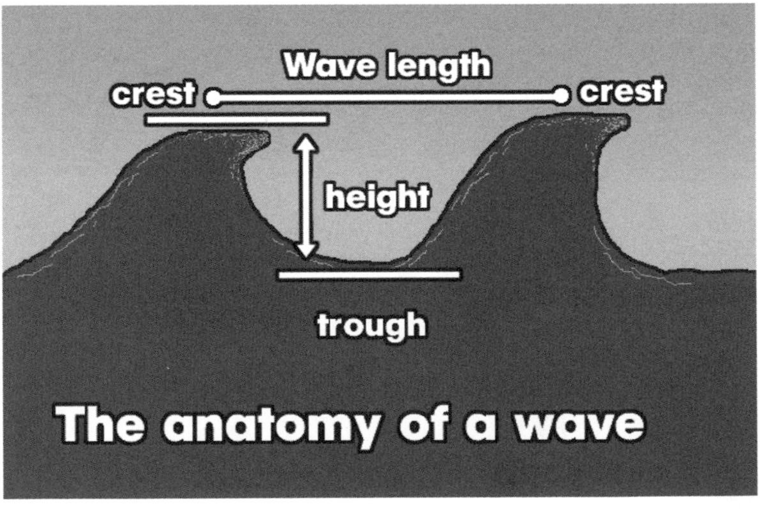

- The **crest** is the top of the wave.

- The **trough** is the bottom of the wave.

- Wave **height** is the vertical distance from the trough to the crest.

- **Wavelength** is the distance between the crest of one wave and the crest of the next.

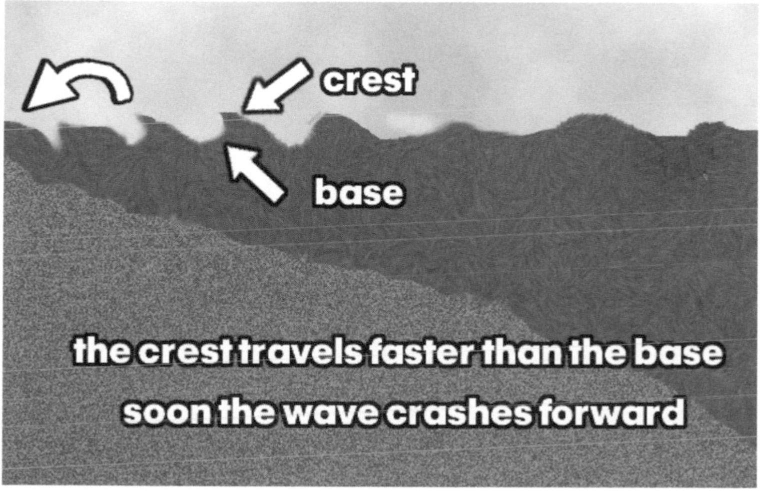
crest
base
the crest travels faster than the base
soon the wave crashes forward

Swells are low, broad, rounded waves that can travel for hundreds of miles without losing much energy. The water in a swell moves around and around in an orbital motion. Swells slow down as they come toward the shallow water of the shore, because the bottom of the orbit followed by the water is interrupted by the shallow sea floor. The interruption of the orbital motion causes the rounded swells to form a sharp crest. The crest travels faster than the base of the wave (which is slowed by the shallow floor) and soon the crest crashes forward.

I laughed, I cried, I think I lost my wallet.

— The King, musing over Bowen's reaction series.

Crashing waves close to the shore are called **breakers**. The water that rushes up on the shore following the crash of a breaker is called **swash**, and when the water slides back into the sea, it's called **backwash**.

1:18:38

As waves approach the beach over a shallowing bottom, the rows of waves usually slow down and bend to a direction more parallel to the shore. This change in direction is referred to as **wave refraction**.

Waves seldom approach the shore head-on. The part of the wave that gets close to the shoreline first slows down as it is affected by the shallow water. The rest of the oncoming wave keeps moving faster and almost catches up with the part that got there first. This is how the wave bends (refracts) to become more parallel to the shore.

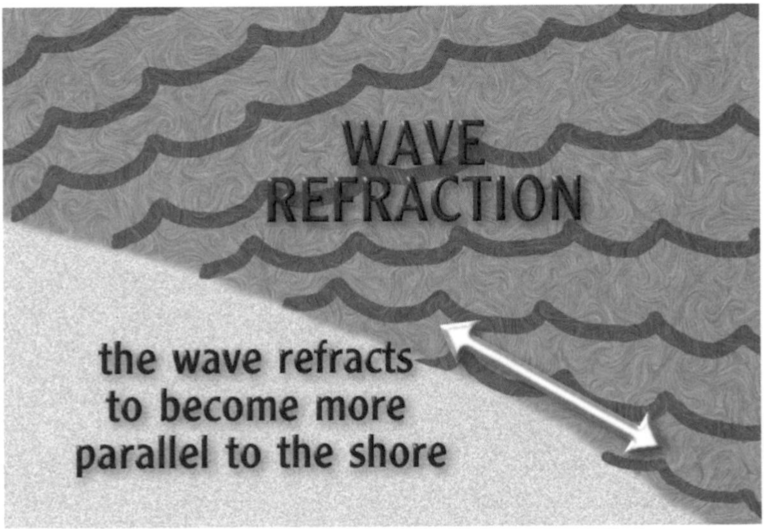
WAVE REFRACTION
the wave refracts to become more parallel to the shore

Despite wave refraction, waves usually hit the shore at an angle and wash back into the ocean at an angle. This angular ebb and flow causes a **longshore current**, running parallel to the shoreline. Sand grains get carried along the shore by **longshore drift**. 1:19:15

A **beach** is a shoreline made up of sand and pebbles. 1:19:31

A **sand bar** is an offshore pile of sand built up by the action of waves or currents. Sand bars are more prevalent in the winter and in bad weather. In the winter, storms cause waves to batter the beaches with greater intensity. The waves pull the sand off the beach and form offshore sand bars. In the summer, the gentler waves carry the sand from the offshore sand bars back to the beach, so the approximate volume of sand near the beach stays the same. 1:19:38

Long sandbars offshore may build up and become **barrier islands**. The Outer Banks of North Carolina are giant sand bar that have become tourist attractions.

Spits are small additions to a beach. They form as a result of longshore drift and project from the shore into the ocean.

VIDEO NOTES V2

SUMMARY

- Shorelines extend from the point where the water gets lowest at low tide to the point where the waves lap the highest during a storm.
- Most waves are created by wind blowing over water, which transfers energy from the moving air to the water.
- The top of a wave is the crest.
- The bottom of a wave is the trough.
- Wavelength is the distance between the crest of one wave and the crest of the next.
- Swells are low, broad, rounded waves. The water in a swell moves around in an orbital motion.
- Breakers are crashing waves close to the shore.
- Swash is the water that rushes up on the shore following the crash of a breaker.
- Backwash is the water that slides back into the sea following the crash of a breaker.

My life is absolute hell.

— Matt May, Director of Sales at Cerebellum, traipsing through the daisies.

STUDY SIDEKICK

- When waves bend to a direction more parallel to the shore, it's called wave refraction. Despite wave refraction, waves usually hit the shore at an angle.

- Longshore drift is the process by which a longshore current carries sand grains along the shore in an angular ebb and flow.

- A beach is a shoreline made up of sand and pebbles.

- A sand bar is an offshore pile of sand built up by the action of waves or currents.

- Long sandbars may build up and become barrier islands such as the Outer Banks of North Carolina.

- A spit is a sandbar that becomes an addition to the beach.

Quiz 15

1. Explain why a wave crests and crashes when it reaches the shore.

2. What is longshore drift?

3. How does the size of a wave increase?

4. A wave crashing on the shore is called a (swell / breaker / refractor) with the water that rushes up the beach known as the (forewave / P-wave / swash) and the water moving back into the ocean called the (backwave / backwater / backwash).

5. Label the parts indicated on the diagram below.

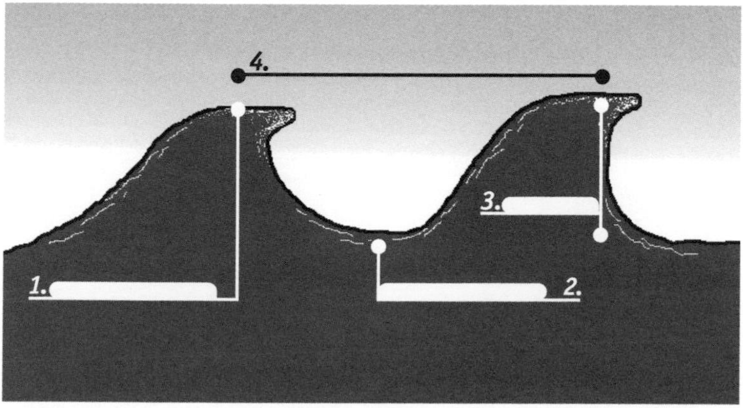

On, bacons, on!

— *Henry IV, Part 1*

6. How does the beach change from season to season?

7. A geologist thinks he has found evidence for an ancient beach. He finds very fine clay size particles and complete, delicate fossils. Is he correct? Why?

8. The Outer Banks in North Carolina are a classic example of a ______________.

9. Define the extent of a shoreline.

Section C: Glaciers

1:21:59

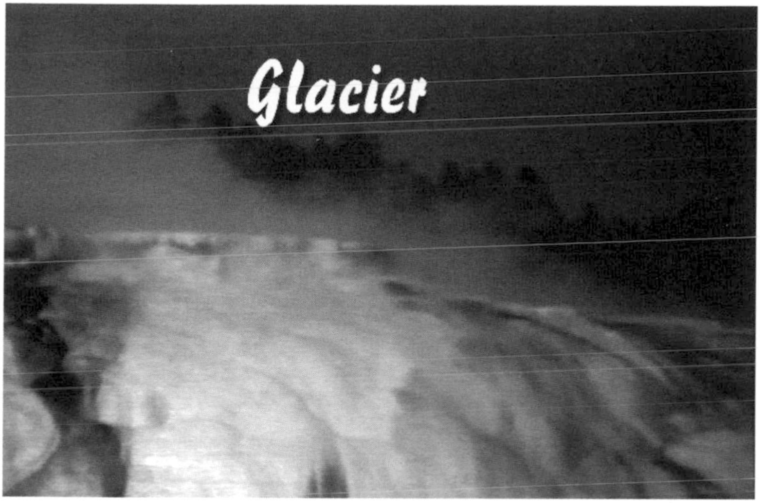

A glacier isn't just any old lump of snow. Specifically, a glacier is a mass of recrystallized snow that moves or has moved in the past. Movement is a glacier's key characteristic; big lumps of ice that don't move are not glaciers. Floating icebergs are not glaciers, because although they move, they do not move across land.

ABOUT 2% OF THE EARTH'S WATER REMAINS FROZEN IN GLACIERS.

Glaciers form from normal snowfall. Newly fallen snow is about 80% air space and only 20% solid snow. Glaciers are created when snow hangs around and compacts instead of melting. As the snow compacts, much of its air space disappears and the compacted snow becomes granular ice called **firn**.

The deeply buried firn compacts even more and becomes glacial ice, which is 90% solids and only 10% air. When the mass of glacial ice gets big enough to move or flow, it's officially a glacier.

How fast do these big ice balls move around? Not very fast at all. Glaciers usually creep forward at very slow rates, often only a few centimeters per day.

HERE'S HOW THEY MOVE:

The pressure resulting from the weight of the accumulated ice makes the ice on the underside of the glacier pliable enough to flow— similar to the way rocks become pliable when they're exposed to a lot of pressure within the Earth. The pressure from the upper ice on the glacier encourages the lower ice to move wherever it can.

Video Notes V2

There are two primary types of glaciers:

- **valley glaciers**
- **continental glaciers**

valley glaciers
usually small glaciers that are confined
within mountain valleys or within
a system of mountain valleys

Valley glaciers are small glaciers confined within mountain valleys or within a system of mountain valleys. They flow downhill from higher elevations to lower elevations. 1:24:16

Continental glaciers are huge, thick, slow-moving ice sheets. Only two continental glaciers exist currently—one in Greenland and one in Antarctica. During the Pleistocene Epoch, early in the Quaternary Period, the Earth experienced an Ice Age of tremendous glaciation. At this time, continental glaciers covered large sections of the continents in the Northern Hemisphere. 1:24:29

By definition, continental glaciers cover at least 50,000 square kilometers, or 19,500 square miles, which is really huge—the average glacier's area is about the size of West Virginia!

CONTINENTAL GLACIERS
huge, thick, slow-moving ice sheets

1:25:04

An **ice cap** is bigger than a valley glacier and smaller than a continental glacier. Ice caps are glaciers that form when a valley glacier in one valley grows so big it expands beyond its own valley, covers the mountain peaks that formerly confined it, and connects with the glacier in the next valley over. The connected valley glaciers form a single ice cap. Ice caps can also form on flat land and on islands. They have the look and flow of continental glaciers, but they are smaller than 19,500 square miles.

ice cap
the connected valley glaciers form a single glacier

No man's pie is freed from your ambitious finger.

— *Henry VIII*

Here are some terms associated with glaciers:

- **Accumulation** is the amount of snow added to a glacier annually.

- **Ablation** is the total amount of ice lost by a glacier annually.

1:25:50

If the downhill end of a glacier moves forward, the glacier is advancing. If a glacier's downhill end moves backwards, the glacier is retreating. The term "retreating" makes it sound like the glacier is moving in opposition to gravity, but that isn't what's happening, since glaciers always move forward. Retreating glaciers move forward with the force of gravity, but they melt faster than they move, so it just *looks* like they are moving backwards.

THE DOWNHILL END OF THE GLACIER IS CALLED THE TERMINUS.

When the downhill end of a glacier doesn't move, we consider the glacier stationary. In other words, it looks like the glacier isn't moving although it is still flowing. If the front of the glacier weren't melting, it would be moving forward; but the front of the glacier disappears at the same rate that the glacier moves, so the glacier doesn't look like it's moving at all.

1:26:55

When glaciers move across land, they can cause large-scale erosion on the ground beneath them. Erosion caused by glaciers includes:

- **U-shaped valleys**
- **striations**
- **cirques**
- **horns**

As valley glaciers move between mountains, they form characteristic **U-shaped valleys**, which are broader across the bottom than the V-shaped valleys formed by streams. Glaciers simply carve out the broad space they need to pass through.

U-shaped valley
formed by a glacier

As a glacier drags rocks along beneath it, the bedrock it moves across gets scratched. These scratches are called **striations**. If the sediment dragged along by the glacier is relatively small and fine, the glacier may polish the bedrock it passes over. The smooth, glacier-polished bedrock glistens in the sunlight.

striations
as a glacier drags rocks
along beneath it
the bedrock it moves
across gets scratched

Don't worry, be nappy.

— Baba Rum Raisin

A **cirque** is a spectacular land formation caused by the movement of valley glaciers. Cirques are amphitheater-shaped hollows carved out of the sides of mountains. We don't understand exactly how cirques form, but they seem be the result of erosion processes such as frost wedging, the opening of rock crevasses due to freezing and thawing water, and general mass wasting. The presence of a glacier speeds up the erosion wearing away the side of a mountain, which gives the mountain a hollow.

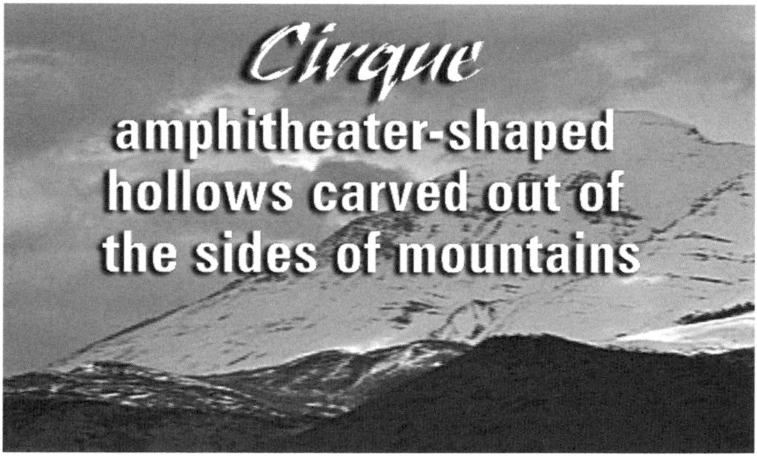
Cirque
amphitheater-shaped hollows carved out of the sides of mountains

When a single mountain has cirques on at least three of its sides, the peak of the mountain takes on a steep-walled pyramid shape. The pyramid-shaped summit is called a **horn**. The peak of the Grand Teton in Wyoming is a horn.

the pyramid-shaped
summit is called a horn

Valley glaciers are often composed of a larger main glacier with smaller glaciers, called **tributary glaciers**, attached to them. The main glacier erodes a large valley beneath it, and the smaller tributary glaciers erode smaller valleys beneath them. The smaller tributary glaciers aren't capable of eroding as large or as deep a valley as the larger main glacier.

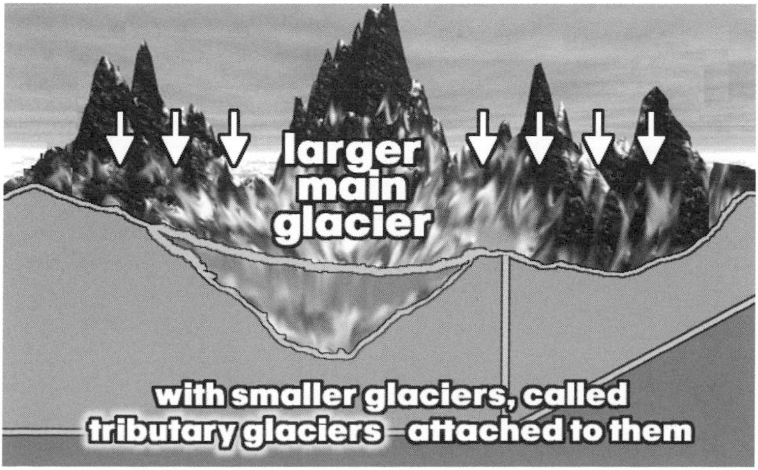
larger
main
glacier
with smaller glaciers, called
tributary glaciers attached to them

Study Sidekick

When glaciers melt away, the smaller valleys formed by the tributary glaciers lie at a higher elevation than the floor of the valley left by the main glacier. These elevated valleys formed by tributary glaciers are called **hanging valleys**. Hanging valleys are often responsible for spectacular waterfalls that drop water from the higher hanging valleys to the main valley below.

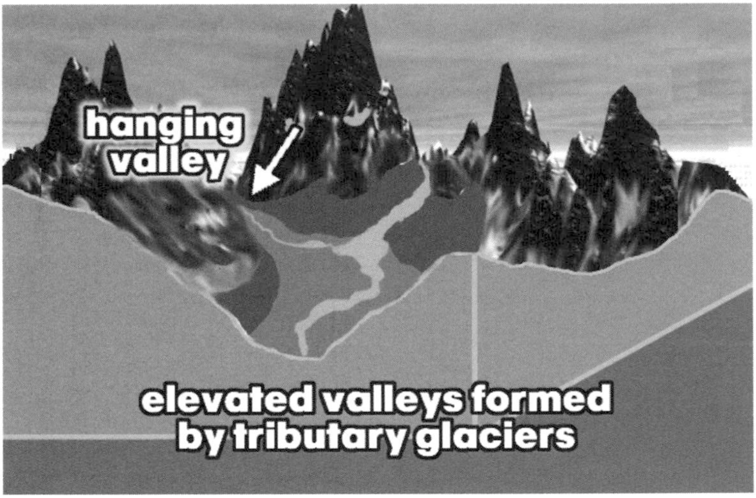

QUIZ

Quiz 16

1. Define accumulation and ablation.

2. What is the difference between an ice cap and a continental glacier?

3. Glacial ice can travel uphill. True or False?

4. How much air is in glacial ice and snow? Give the percentage.

5. Striations are used to indicate the directions of flow of glaciers that existed in the past. What are striations and how are they made?

6. A glaciated valley is typically U/ V/ W / X shaped.

7. The terminus of XYZ glacier has not moved for 10 years. This means that the glacier has stopped moving. True or False? Explain.

8. After the last ice age all the continental glaciers disappeared. True or False?

9. What is a horn?

10. What is a hanging valley?

THE ANSWER MAN

The Answer Man is dedicated to alleviating the worries of his fellow Cerebellum employees. Each day, he receives hundreds of letters from co-workers. We have reprinted some of them here with The Answer Man's responses. We hope they can be helpful to you, too.

Dear Answer Man,
What do you get if you splice together Dana Carvey and a wooden spoon?

A three-week Vegas show as Vlad the Impaler of the Stars.

Dear Answer Man!
Where is Jimmy Hoffa?

Wherever you were last playing with him.
By the way, you don't have to shout.

Dear Answer Man:
Where do the sox that never find their way out of the washing machine go?

Examine your question. You could have answered it yourself. The SOCKS are still in the washer.

Dear Answer Man:
Who really shot Jack Kennedy.

No, the Who did not really shoot Jack Kennedy. However, the Who can see for miles and miles.

Study Sidekick

Dear Answer Man:
Is their life on other planets?
If yes, do you think Jodie Foster will ever really meet them?

There most certainly is intelligent life on other planets. Jodie Foster? No.

Dear Answer Man:
Where, oh where has my little dog gone, oh where oh where can he be?

I have located your dog, one Fluffy. Fluffy took the 10:15 Metroliner to New York last night and spent most of the ride in the dining car, where he met another dog named Rex. Together, Rex and Fluffy planned the armed robbery of Jelinski's liquor store in Queens. At approximately 3:40 PM, Fluffy and Rex entered the liquor store. The cashier thought that the dogs looked suspicious, so she rang the silent alarm. Police arrived at the scene six minutes later, to find the dogs maliciously gnawing on the cashier's ankle. Rex and Fluffy were taken into custody. Fluffy is now in the third precinct lock-up, waiting for a hearing.

So, in the most literal sense, Fluffy is in New York.
In a more figurative sense, Fluffy has gone down the sordid path to crime and debasement.
I hope that helps.

Do YOU have a question for the Answer Man?
Send your questions about life, love, and the world in general to:

The Answer Man
2890 Emma Lee Street
Falls Church, VA 22042

STRESS RELIEF

Earth Word Scramble

Look through the scrambled letters for each of the words listed to the right. Circle each letter of each word as you find it. When you circle all of the letters of all the words, there will be some letters left over. Make a list of the unused letters and then unscramble them to solve the puzzle. Here's a hint: The solution to the puzzle has 44 letters, and it's a new twist on an old tongue twister.

G	E	O	L	O	G	Y	D	C	S	T	N	E	M	I	D	E	S	R	L
R	I	C	A	M	B	R	I	A	N	O	O	N	A	C	L	O	V	E	A
M	O	U	N	I	F	O	R	M	I	T	A	R	I	A	N	I	S	M	T
A	I	C	M	L	Z	F	M	T	P	O	R	O	G	E	N	E	S	I	S
N	T	N	K	O	A	L	A	O	N	E	Z	P	P	R	E	A	N	N	A
T	R	K	E	S	U	T	L	P	L	O	C	A	A	R	K	R	M	E	O
L	I	L	S	R	L	N	E	A	R	T	H	Q	U	A	K	E	I	H	C
E	A	A	M	A	A	R	T	E	W	O	E	S	D	T	S	Z	G	E	U
P	S	J	S	E	E	L	N	A	E	T	S	N	S	O	A	U	N	R	R
S	S	E	N	D	R	A	H	H	I	E	O	U	Z	M	C	A	E	C	R
I	I	D	N	S	H	C	O	P	R	N	R	O	G	E	I	N	O	U	E
C	C	A	C	P	U	E	A	P	P	C	I	A	F	H	O	H	U	L	N
Y	E	D	O	I	S	R	E	L	O	C	M	F	C	O	Z	C	S	E	T
M	N	R	N	L	S	O	F	O	L	G	E	A	L	I	O	S	I	S	C
R	E	A	T	A	I	S	L	A	E	I	L	B	O	U	N	D	A	R	Y
A	C	I	I	O	E	I	A	T	C	A	T	A	U	A	E	T	A	L	P
M	O	N	N	C	N	O	V	R	P	E	I	C	C	H	C	O	P	E	K
S	E	A	E	G	G	N	A	P	U	P	N	I	T	I	S	O	P	E	D
E	L	G	N	I	T	S	A	W	P	J	G	D	T	Y	E	L	L	A	V
O	U	E	T	S	I	H	C	S	F	F	U	T	A	I	N	R	E	H	S

ACID
ANNA
APPALACHIAN
BOUNDARY
CAMBRAIN
CENOZOIC
COAL
COASTAL
CONTINENT
COOLING
CRUST
CURRENT
DEJA
DEPOSIT
DRAINAGE
EARTHQUAKE
EOCENE
EPOCH
EROSION
FOOTWALL
GEOLOGY
GLACIER
GNEISS
HARDNESS
HERCULES
HERNIA
IGNEOUS
JURASSIC
LAVA
MAGMA
MANTLE
MEANDER
MELTING
MERCALLI
MESOZOIC
MINERAL
MOLTEN
MOUNTAIN
OROGENESIS
PAHOEHOE
PHANEROZOIC
PLATEAU
PRESSURE
ROCK
SALTATION
SASSAFRAS
SCHIST
SCHNAUZER
SEDIMENT
SMARMY
SOIL
SURFACE
TALE
TRIASSIC
TUFF
UNIFORMITARIANISM
VALLEY
VOLCANO
WASTING

Eartho Crosso

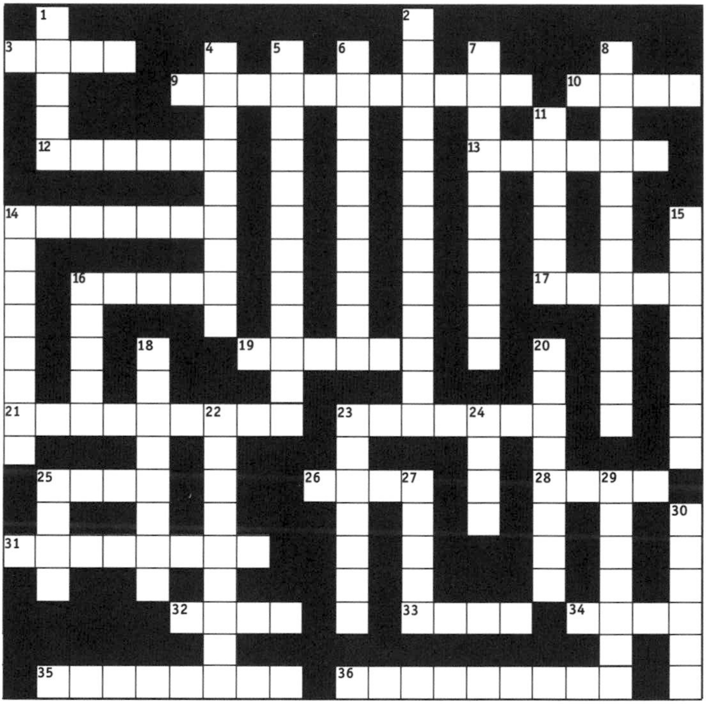

ACROSS

3. ice not plant
9. rock dome that peels like an onion
10. magma not nacho
12. Hawaiian volcano edifice
13. entrusive igneous blobular body
14. hazelnut
16. bird droppings
17. alcohol homonym
19. central layers of the Earth
21. upward arching fold
23. crashing wave
25. volcanoes and drunks do this
26. think sand and happy hour
28. line dividing fold
31. a terrible lizard
32. call it "soil"
33. a syncline-looking thing in the bathroom
34. the sediment a stream caries is its...
35. filbert
36. "without form" (blobular)

DOWN

1. discordant igneous intrusions
2. layer of partially molten rock
4. a type of chemical weathering
5. large-grained sedimentary rock
6. German organ sausage
7. puddles don't have any
8. sediment basin – not a toilet
11. boisterous snorting laughter
14. plagioclase is part of this group
15. breakage along a plane – it's no joke
16. gutteral utterance when you lift a rock
18. retreating wave or the end of a soda
20. chick pea
22. when igneous pushes its way in
23. tangled stream or Igor the writer
24. he who falls over rocks regularly
25. don't call it dirt
27. concordant igneous intrusions
29. rocks that come from lava or magma
30. a cone with two scoops of lava

TEST YOURSELF

PRACTICE EXAM 2

"Geo" is a hip and swingin' way to say "geology." It's also an affordable car.

— Larry the Lounge Lizard

1. The three types of plate boundaries are

   A) continental, convergent, and divergent.

   B) continental, oceanic, and lithospheric.

   C) convergent, divergent, and transform.

   D) convergent, oceanic, and volcanic.

   E) continental, oceanic, and asthenospheric.

2. The principal reason why Wegner's theory for Continental Drift was rejected by other scientists was because Wegner stated that

   A) mountain ranges on different continents were different ages.

   B) fossils were different on every continents.

   C) land bridges occurred under the surface of all oceans.

   D) continental crust moved through oceanic crust.

   E) the drift of the continents was affected by the moon.

3. If the continents were once together, rocks and mountain ranges on the margins of each should have

   A) different rock sequences.

   B) different ages.

C) glacial deposits.

D) the same structural trends.

E) fossils.

4. New oceanic crust is formed at

A) convergent plate boundaries.

B) transform plate boundaries.

C) normal plate boundaries.

D) reverse plate boundaries.

E) divergent plate boundaries.

5. The majority of earthquakes occur in zones located within

A) the mantle.

B) the Mediterranean-Asiatic Belt.

C) the Circum-Pacific Belt.

D) the Mid-Atlantic Ridge.

E) the Circum-Mediterranean Belt.

6. S-waves, also known as shear waves, move material ________ to the direction of the wave and can pass through ________.

A) parallel, solids

B) parallel, gases

C) horizontal, solids and gases

D) perpendicular, solids

E) perpendicular, the core

TEST YOURSELF

7. The two main types of seismic waves are

   A) surfing and P-waves.

   B) primary and secondary waves.

   C) surface and body waves.

   D) shear waves and cheer waves.

   E) P-waves and L-waves.

8. The epicenter of an earthquake is always underground.

   A) True

   B) False

9. Which of the following structural layers of the Earth is liquid?

   A) mantle

   B) crust

   C) inner core

   D) outer core

   E) asthenosphere

10. The thinnest and lowest volume structural layer of the Earth is the

    A) lithosphere.

    B) outer core.

    C) asthenosphere.

    D) mantle.

    E) crust.

May you live all the days of your life.

— Jonathan Swift

OTHER IMPORTANT STUFF

Stuff 1: The Geologic Time Scale

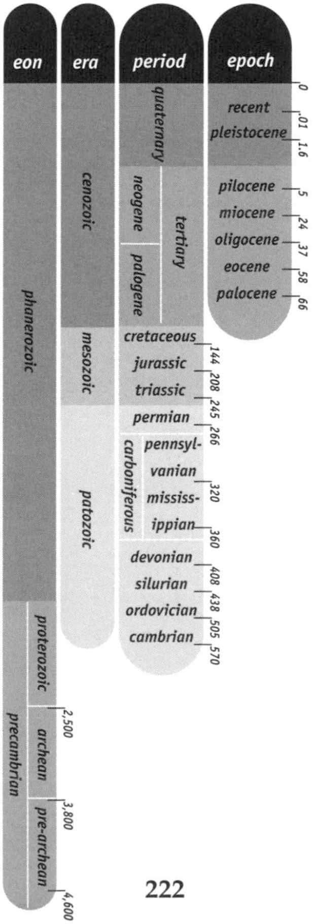

Stuff 2: Radiometric Dating

Here comes a little more chemistry…But quit whimpering, it's just a quick look at an important concept.

Radiometric dating is a type of absolute dating scientists use to assign rocks a numerical age. Remember the difference between absolute dating and relative dating: Relative dating only places things or events in *sequential order*—it doesn't assign a numerical age. Geologists use what they know about nuclear properties and the behavior of atoms to assign an age in years to rocks.

All matter is made up of atoms. **Atoms** are composed of protons, neutrons, and electrons. The protons and neutrons reside in the nucleus, and the electrons encircle the nucleus.

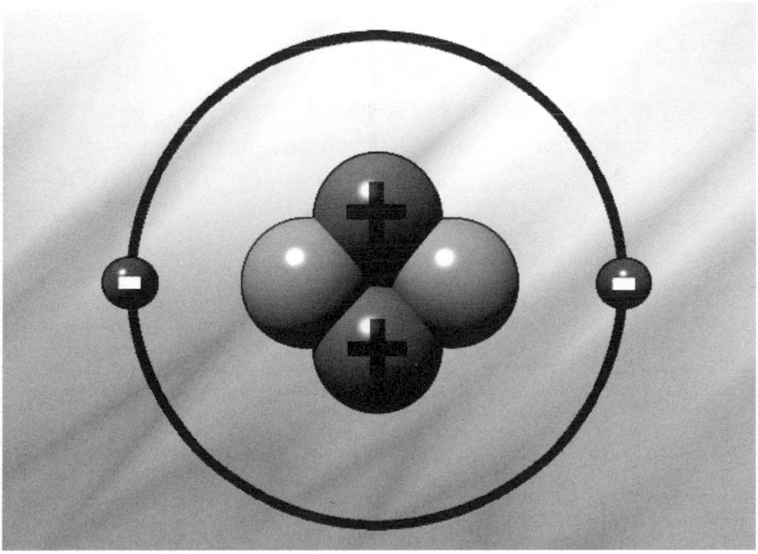

- The number of protons in the nucleus is called the *atomic number*. In helium, the atomic number is 2, because helium has two protons.

- The number of protons plus the number of neutrons in the nucleus is called the *atomic mass*. In helium, the atomic mass is 4, because helium has 2 protons and 2 neutrons in its nucleus.

Not all atoms of the same element have the same number of neutrons. These atoms are called **isotopes**.

Regular hydrogen has no neutrons. The hydrogen isotope called "deuterium" has one neutron and the isotope "tritium" has two neutrons. These are all hydrogen atoms, but they represent different forms of hydrogen.

Some isotopes are stable. In other words, they don't spontaneously lose or gain any protons, neutrons, or electrons. Other isotopes spontaneously decay to a more stable form. When they decay, they shed or take on subatomic particles (protons, neutrons, or electrons) until they reach a form that is stable. It is the *rate* of this decay that we use to determine the absolute age of things through radiometric dating.

OTHER STUFF

Isotopes decay from an unstable "parent" to a stable "daughter" by either emitting particles or energy. There are three types of decay an isotope can undergo.

- ▲ **alpha decay**: the isotope loses 2 protons and 2 neutrons
- ▲ **beta decay**: the isotope loses 1 electron
- ▲ **gamma decay:** emission of a high-energy photon

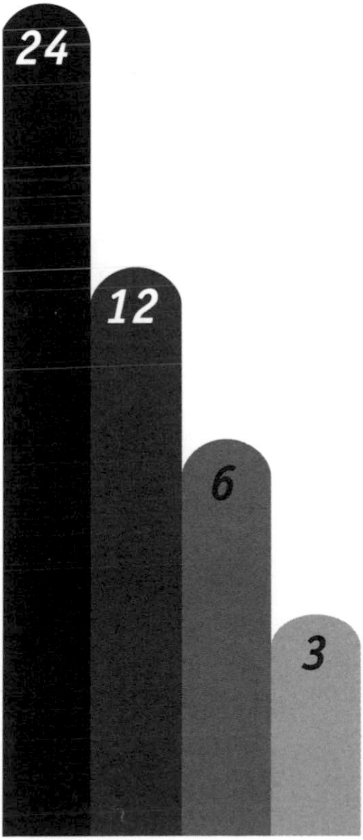

Some isotopes only undergo one of these transformations to become a stable "daughter." Others undergo ten or more transformations to become stable. The amount of time it takes for half of the atoms in the substance to decay and become the daughter form is the atom's **half-life**. Here's a very simple example.

Say we have a substance that contains 48 atoms. When 24 of these atoms decay to a more stable form, the substance has gone through its first half-life transformation. Now we have 24 parent atoms and 24 stable daughter atoms. When half of the remaining parent atoms decay (12 atoms), the substance has gone through its second half-life transformation. Now we have 12 parent atoms and 36 stable daughter atoms. When 6 of the remaining parent atoms decay to the stable daughter form, the substance has gone through its third half-life transformation. Get it? Good.

There will always be some of the parent isotope remaining, but the amount can get too small for us to measure. If we can accurately measure the ratio of parent isotope to daughter isotope, we can get the age of the rock. This is the gist of radiometric dating.

The carbon isotope known as carbon-14 has a half-life of 5,730 years. Carbon-14 is an unstable isotope created by a reaction in the atmosphere. Every living thing takes in radioactive carbon-14. (Fortunately it is not enough to harm us.) When a tree or animal dies, it stops taking in carbon-14. The isotope inside the dead organism decays and is not replenished anymore. The half-life clock has started and the ratio of carbon-14 to stable carbon-12 begins changing. The measurement of this ratio can then be used to determine when the animal died or the tree was cut down.

For us to date a rock, the radioactive isotopes in the rock must have a long half-life: such as uranium, which has a half-life of 4.5 billion years, or potassium, which has a half-life of 1.3 billion years. Since different minerals are composed of different elements, geologists use various dating methods according to the minerals of which the rock is made.

Stuff 3: More Laws and Principles

They're my dogs and they can eat and run if they want to.

—Old Tracker Guy from *Rambo*

Unconformities are gaps in the geological record. There is no one place on Earth where a complete sequence of rocks exists showing the progression from the Archean until today. The gaps in the sequence are periods of non-deposition, usually when the land is above sea level.

The Principle of Unconformities deals with three types of unconformities:

- **disconformities**
- **angular unconformities**
- **nonconformities**

Disconformities are parallel strata of older and younger rock. The strata may look as if they were deposited one right on top of another in logical sequence, but absolute dating or examination of the fossil record shows that the lower part of the strata is much older than the top part, indicating that some part of the sedimentary sequence is missing. Disconformities occur when there is a period in which no deposition occurs, or when a deposit between an older and a younger layer erodes away.

This block shows a disconformity. Here's a simple geological history explaining how the block may have formed.

1. Sedimentary layers 1, 2, 3, and 4 are deposited. Layer 1 is the oldest and 4 is the youngest.

2. The area is uplifted and eroded. Some layers erode away.

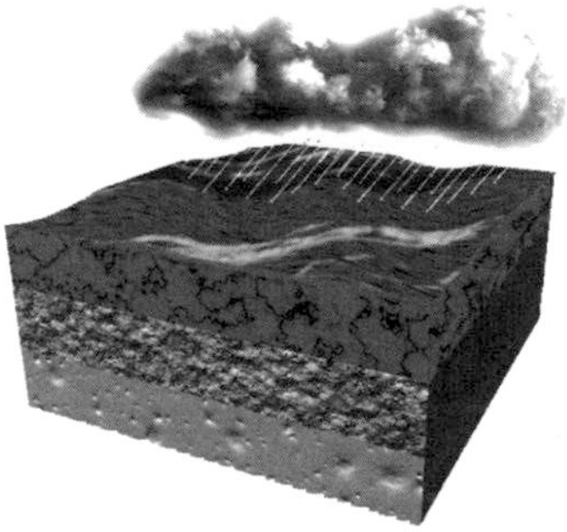

3. The area is submerged and deposition of sediments begins again.

4. There is an unconformity (a gap in the geologic record) between the third and the new fourth layer of sediment. The original fourth layer of sediment eroded away during the period of uplift and erosion.

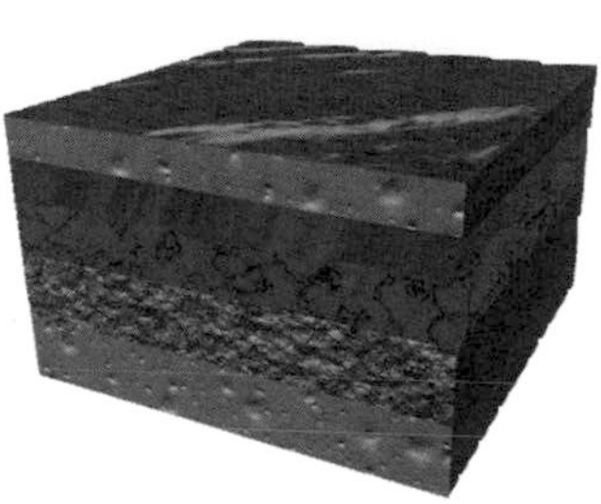

Other Stuff

Angular Unconformities

Angular unconformities are characterized by older, tilted layers of rock covering a younger, horizontal layer.

Here's a possible geological history of this block:

1. Sedimentary layers 1, 2, 3, 4, 5, and 6 are deposited. Layer 1 is the oldest and 6 is the youngest.

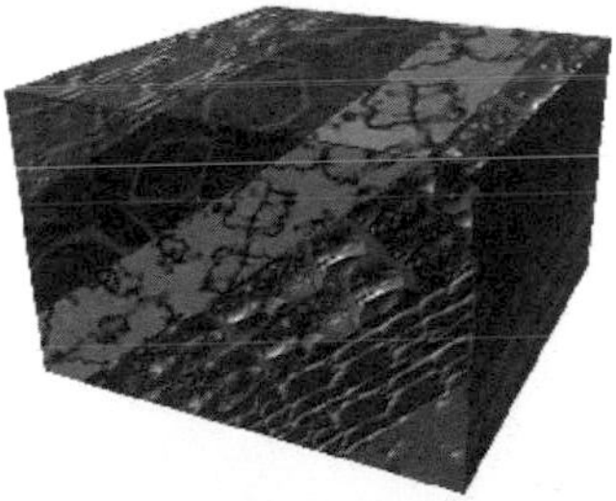

2. The area is tilted by uplift and the top of the layers is eroded away.

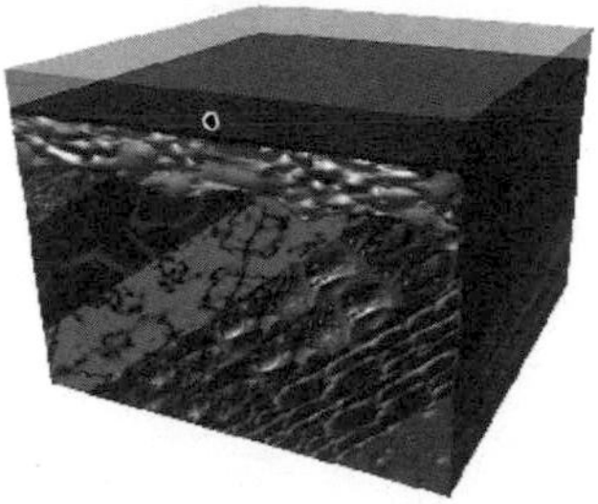

3. The area is submerged and sediments are deposited horizontally on top of the older (tilted and eroded) beds.

Nonconformities

Nonconformities involve sedimentary layers deposited over an eroded igneous intrusion or layer of metamorphic rock.

The geological history of this block would be:

1. The igneous or metamorphic base rocks are uplifted and tilted.

2. Erosion occurs.

3. The area is submerged and sediments are deposited on top of the eroded base rocks.

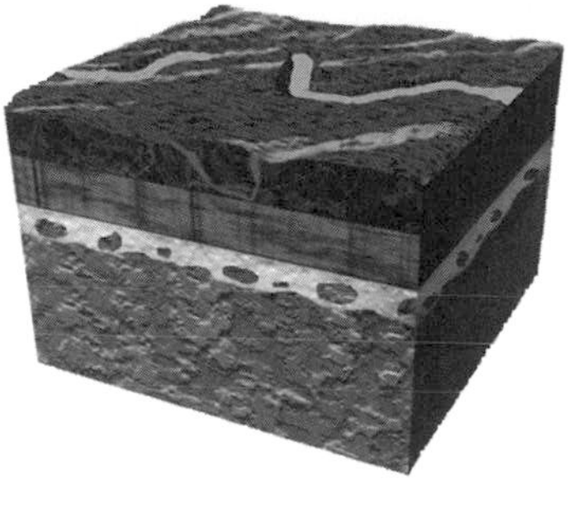

Other Stuff

Stuff 4: More about Minerals

Silicate Structures

Silicon and oxygen are the most common elements in the Earth's crust. Over 40% of the common minerals are silicates, so your professor may want you to know more about their structure.

The fundamental silicate building unit is the silicon-oxygen tetrahedron. It's called a tetrahedron because it has four sides. It consists of one silicon ion that has a positive charge and four oxygen ions, each with a negative charge. The four large oxygen ions surround the small silicate ion. The silica tetrahedron is held together by both ionic bonds (the attraction between positive and negative charges) and covalent bonds (the sharing of electrons between atoms).

The overall charge of the silica tetrahedron is −4, so its oxygens have the ability to bond with positively charged ions, even other silicon ions. The tetrahedron forms the basis of the silicate mineral structures.

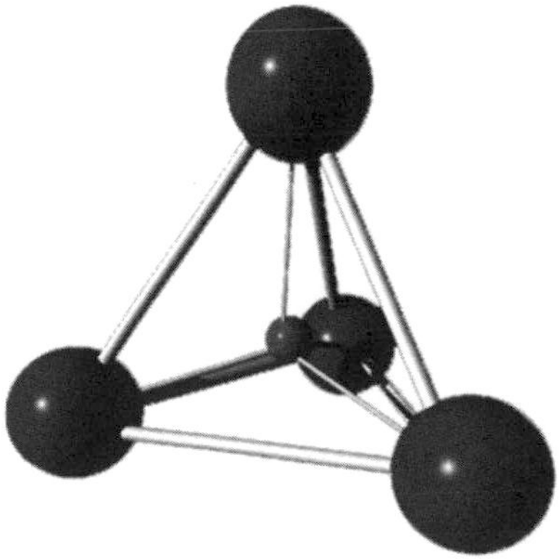

Stuff 5: Other Physical Properties

1. **Specific gravity**: Some minerals feel heavy, such as galena, which is an ore for lead.

2. **Taste**: Some minerals have a distinctive taste, such as halite or rock salt. The Standard Deviants do not recommend you go around tasting all the rocks you see. You don't know where those rocks have been.

3. **Feel**: Some minerals, such as graphite, feel greasy.

4. **Magnetism**: Magnetite is the only mineral that is strongly magnetic.

5. **Smell**: The mineral sphalerite smells of sulfur when you powder it.

6. **Reaction**: The mineral calcite reacts with weak hydrochloric acid (HCl) to give off carbon dioxide gas (CO_2). It fizzes.

Stuff 6: A List of the Main Rock-Forming Minerals

Hint: "Primary Occurrence" refers to the type of rock (metamorphic, igneous, or sedimentary) in which we generally find the specific rock-building mineral.

Name	Composition	Primary Occurrence
Olivine	$(Mg,Fe)2SiO_4$	igneous/ metamorphic
Pyroxene (Augite)	$(Ca,Fe,Mg)\ 2Si_2O_6$	igneous/ metamorphic
Amphibole (Hornblende)	hydrous Na, Ca, Mg, Fe, Al chain silicate	igneous/metamorphic (rare in sedimentary rock)
Mica (Muscovite, Biotite)	Hydrous K, Al, Mg, Fe sheet silicate	all rock types
Quartz	SiO_2	all rock types
Feldspar 1. Potassium feldspar	$KAlSi_3O_8$	all rock types

Good friends share their chapstick.

— Opus, *Outland*

2. Plagioclase feldspar	$NaAlSi_3O_8$ $CaAl_2Si_2O_8$	igneous/ metamorphic
Clay minerals	Hydrous phases	sedimentary
Calcite	$CaCO_3$	sedimentary
Dolomite	$CaMg(CO_3)_2$	sedimentary
Gypsum	$CaSO_42H_2O$	sedimentary
Halite (salt)	NaCl	sedimentary

Other Stuff

Stuff 7: More on Magma and Plutons

1. There are several other types of plutonic igneous bodies, including:

- laccoliths: mushroom-shaped plutons which may be any size

- volcanic necks: plutons that were once part of a volcano (remember, magma that cools slowly beneath the surface is considered plutonic)

2. Here's a table giving nifty information about the four igneous compositions (felsic, intermediate, mafic, and ultramafic).

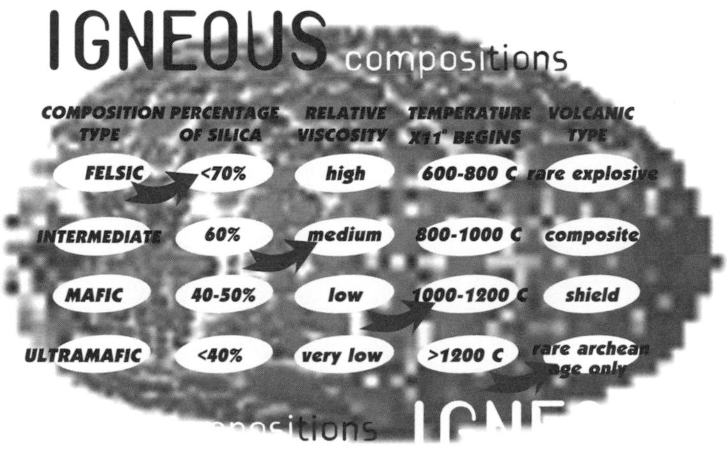

IGNEOUS compositions

COMPOSITION TYPE	PERCENTAGE OF SILICA	RELATIVE VISCOSITY	TEMPERATURE X11' BEGINS	VOLCANIC TYPE
FELSIC	<70%	high	600-800 C	rare explosive
INTERMEDIATE	60%	medium	800-1000 C	composite
MAFIC	40-50%	low	1000-1200 C	shield
ULTRAMAFIC	<40%	very low	>1200 C	rare archean age only

Stuff 8: Weathering and Acid Rain

A major environmental concern today is acid rain. Betcha didn't know that all rain is slightly acidic. Water reacts with carbon dioxide in the atmosphere and makes weak **carbonic acid**. This gives natural rainwater a pH of 5.6. The pH of pure water is 7, which is neutral.

Acid rain is *more* acidic than normal rainfall. Industry and coal burning has put sulfur in the atmosphere. The sulfur reacts with water in the atmosphere to form sulfuric acid, a much stronger acid than the weak carbonic acid that rainwater normally contains. Rain polluted with sulfuric acid may have a pH of 2.5 or less. That makes some acid rain as strongly acidic as vinegar or lemon juice!

OTHER STUFF

Stuff 9: More about the Interior of the Earth and Seismic Waves

The transition zone is 400 to 1,050 kilometers down. As seismic waves travel through this zone, they experience several changes in velocity, but overall they get progressively faster. Geologists believe that this change in seismic wave velocity implies that the deeper the waves travel, the denser the rocks and minerals they encounter.

Speaking of feelings, darned if I don't feel like a Boeing 747.

— A member of Earthbound Birds Anonymous, *Outland*

Caution: Extremely Hot Facts about the Earth's Core

SIZE:	slightly larger than Mars
LOCATION:	3486 km (2167 miles) into the Earth
VOLUME:	$\frac{1}{6}$th of the Earth's volume
MASS:	$\frac{1}{3}$rd of the Earth's mass
PRESSURE:	3 million atmospheres
TEMPERATURE:	7600° Celsius
COMPOSITION:	iron and nickel (which are ultra dense) with a little silicon and sulfur

Study Sidekick

Why Geologists Think This Is the Composition of the Core

1. This model fits seismic wave data that scientists generated experimentally in a laboratory and then extrapolated to match the Earth's incredibly high temperatures and pressures.

2. The core is believed to be similar to metallic alloy of iron and nickel found in some meteorites.

3. It fits computer modeling of the densities needed to recreate the mass of the whole Earth.

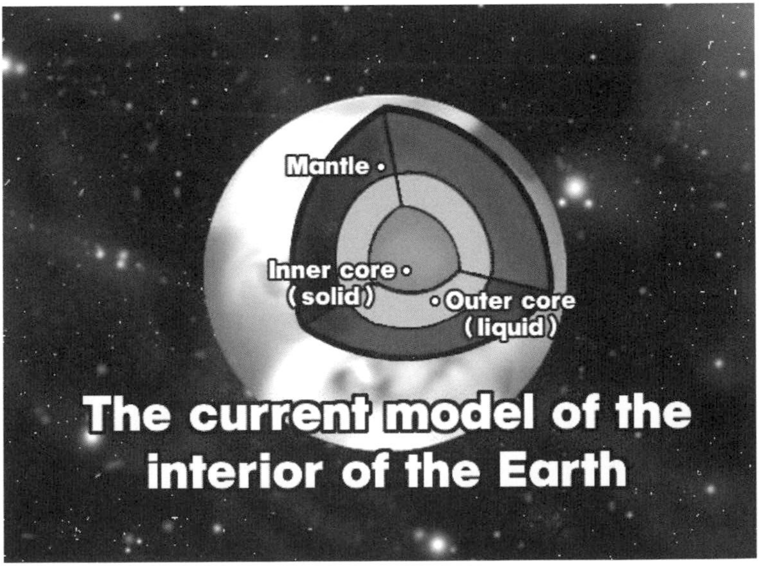

OTHER STUFF

Stuff 10: More Stuff about Streams

How Rain Becomes a Stream

Picture this: It's raining on a mountain. When the rainwater first starts flowing down the mountain, it's just flowing over the land and is not in a channel. When this water encounters a depression in the land, it flows into it and erodes the depression into a narrow depression called a rill. The rill is the start of the transport area—the area that is becoming the channel of a stream.

The forming channel becomes progressively larger, and turns into a tributary that will flow into a **trunk stream**, which is the main stream in a drainage system. Voilà. The draining water has become a stream, and now heads for the ocean.

The mouth of the stream is the point where it enters an ocean or a lake. At this point, streams generally separate into distributaries. The stream's mouth is the stream's base level, the lowest point it can attain before it flows into a larger body of water. Lakes, dams, and waterfalls are temporary base levels; the ultimate base level is the ocean.

The longitudinal profile of a stream is the cross-section of a stream channel from the headwaters (the origin) to the mouth (the end where it flows into a larger body of water). A stream channel is characteristically concave. In an ideal situation, a stream will attain a clean concave profile and will flow just swiftly enough to transport its sediment. A stream in this ideal situation is in a state of equilibrium, and is called a graded stream.

The true test of maturity is not one's age, but how one reacts to awakening in the midtown area in his shorts.

— Woody Allen

In nature, streams are rarely in equilibrium. Even if they reach equilibrium for a while, they seldom stay that way very long, because the action of streams is very dynamic: a stream's profile can change almost instantaneously. For example, increased rainfall can increase a stream's flow dramatically, causing more erosion. Erosion widens and changes the shape of the channel, so the stream can carry more sediment and remove deposits where the stream slowed down or was blocked. Common events such as rainstorms can quickly change a stream's longitudinal profile.

Channel Shape

If a stream's channel is deep and smooth, the water moves slowly, with the molecules bopping along happily. This type of flow is called a laminar flow. A stream with laminar flow has little erosion potential, because the water is not beating on the channel and the land around it with great erosion potential, because the water beats up against the channel.

The **velocity** of a stream is the measurement of how far the water travels per foot per second. Velocity is not uniform in the channel. It is slowest at the sides and the bottom of the channel due to the friction and greatest just below the surface in the center of a straight channel, because there's not much to get in the way of the flow there.

Discharge is the volume of water that goes past a certain point in a stream over a certain period of time. It is measured in cubic feet per second. Here's how geologists calculate discharge:

$$\text{discharge} = \text{area of channel (width} \times \text{depth)} \times \text{velocity}$$

OTHER STUFF

The discharge of the Mississippi River is 600,000 cubic feet of water per second, and the discharge of the Amazon River is 7,000,000 cubic feet per second. The amount of water that flows past one point on the Amazon in one day is enough to supply New York City with water for five years!

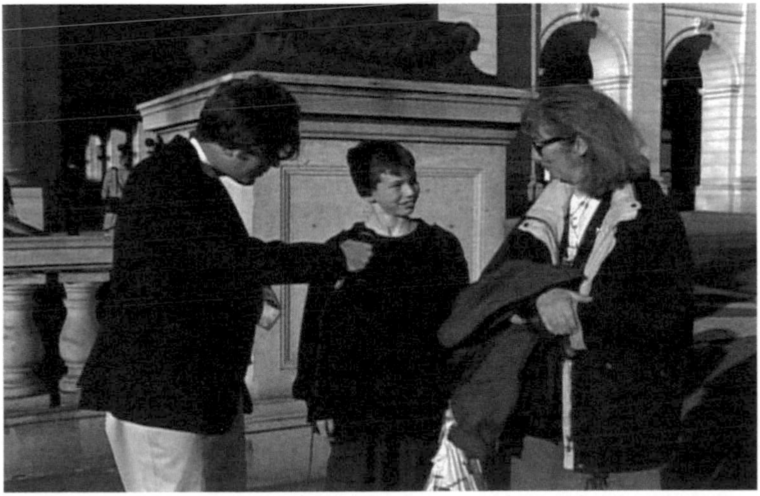

THE STANDARD DEVIANTS

STUDY SIDEKICK

I still think a ceiling is essential to a good dorm room.

–Mister Seventies

THE STANDARD DEVIANTS PRESENT

YOUR dorm room ESSENTIALS

A WEE LIST FOR YE, LADDIES AND LASSIES

- ★ **alarm clock**
- ◎ **cactus (don't have to water it)**
- ◎ **dictionary, thesaurus**
- ◎ **throw rug**
- ◎ **can opener**
- ◎ **cereal bowl + spoon and fork (spork is okay)**
- ◎ **basketball**
- ◎ **bedsheets (3 sets so you don't have to wash 'em)**
- ◎ **shower caddy + soap + shampoo**
- ◎ **comb, nail clippers**
- ◎ **1,000-count box of paper toilet seat covers**
- ◎ **towels (3 sets—see above)**
- ★ **zit cream**
- ◎ **4 years worth of deodorant**
- ◎ **personal bathroom attendant**
- ◎ **TV + VCR + stereo (small of size, large of wattage)**
- ◎ **CDs**
- ◎ **more CDs**
- ◎ **CDs you don't even listen to (they're a status symbol)**
- ◎ **lava lamp or equivalent**
- ◎ **mini-fridge for sammiches**
- ◎ **extra-large coffee mug**
- ◎ **power strips to plug into extension cords**
- ◎ **extension cords to plug into power strips to plug into extension cords**
- ◎ **hair dryer**
- ◎ **computer, blender, toaster oven**
- ◎ **hot-air popcorn popper**
- ◎ **powered juicer**

Other Stuff

◎ breadmaker
◎ any other appliance to plug into extension cord plugged into power strips
◎ extra fuses, fire blankets
◎ clothes (3 sets—see above)
◎ bathrobe
◎ underwear (6 sets—you can wear dirty clothes longer than dirty underwear)
◎ shoes (2 pair—one that looks good, one that feels good)
◎ prom outfit, not yet dry-cleaned
◎ workout outfit (spandex, sweats, or both)
◎ 1920s-style bathingsuit in case of group shower + flip-flops
◎ pictures of your most attractive high school friends (to curry favor and garner status with roommates)
★ posters for walls (your choice:beer poster or post-WWII French people kissing)
◎ sticky stuff to stick posters to wall
◎ white-out (to fill in holes in wall at the end of the year)
◎ dry-erase message board + markers
◎ answering machine with clever outgoing message
◎ lighter (if you don't need it, someone will)
◎ blacklight
◎ amusing Co-ed Naked t-shirt
◎ yo-yo
◎ camera to be stolen at a later date
◎ commitment to body piercing
◎ a book about massage (★ or a video—video is better)
◎ The Road Less Travelled
◎ Dr. Seuss books (one of which must be Oh! The Places You'll Go)
◎ funny stuff to e-mail
◎ ability to type :) very quickly
◎ condoms (to give to your roommates in the middle of the night)
◎ condoms (clever replacement for party balloons)
◎ condoms (last-minute Halloween costume)
◎ Betamax VCR (it's better, really)
★ bicycle/ rollerblades/ skateboard/ snowboard/ ouija board (depending on region)
◎ car to park out front
◎ waterguns (at least 2)
◎ *Little House on the Prairie* tape collection

- ◎ lawnmower
- ◎ megaphone
- ★ the jive
- ◎ white hat with college name on it
- ◎ hot tub, lounge chair (don't worry, you'll find room)
- ◎ arcade-style video games
- ★ fake ID so you can rent a car
- ◎ pink flamingo lawn ornaments
- ◎ Christmas lights (white, multi-colored, or mini jalapeños)
- ◎ street signs
- ◎ boom box
- ★ frisbee
- ◎ pencils (at least one)

ANSWERS

Here, kitty, kitty.

— Norman Bates

Quiz 1:

1. Relative and absolute.

2. 4,600 million years; 4.6 billion years.

3. Middle life; Triassic, Jurassic, Cretaceous.

4. **False**. Mammals have only been around since the Mesozoic.

5. Physical geologists study what materials the Earth is made of, and what's happening on and beneath the Earth's surface.

6. Fish.

7.

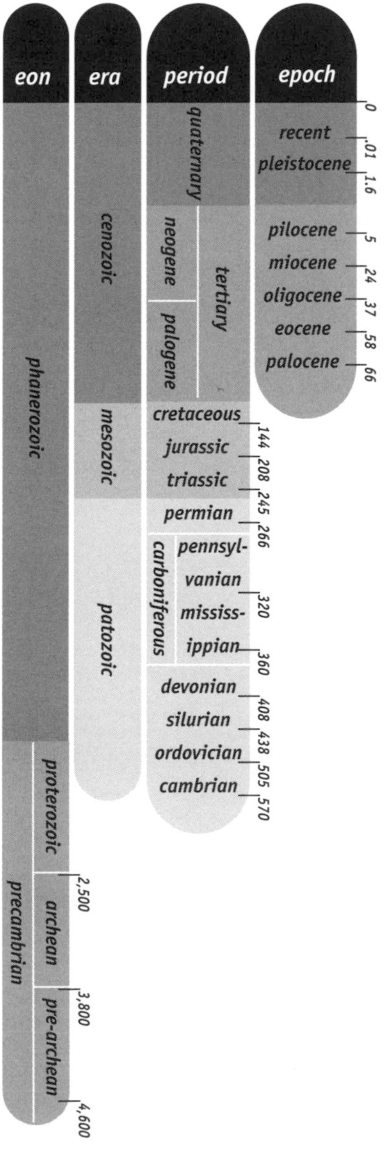
eon
era
period
epoch
0
recent
.01
pleistocene
1.6
quaternary
cenozoic
neogene
palogene
tertiary
pilocene
5
miocene
24
oligocene
37
eocene
58
palocene
66
phanerozoic
mesozoic
cretaceous
144
jurassic
208
triassic
245
permian
266
carboniferous
pennsyl-
vanian
320
mississ-
ippian
360
patozoic
devonian
408
silurian
438
ordovician
505
cambrian
570
proterozoic
2,500
archean
3,800
pre-archean
4,600
precambrian

ANSWERS

Quiz 2:

1. Sedimentary rocks contain little pieces of stuff that happened to be around at the time the rocks formed.

2. According to uniformitarianism, we can figure that a volcano eruption now is pretty much like a volcano eruption was a million years ago. Uniformitarianism helps us understand the behavior of past volcanic activity.

3. We can assume something happened that was powerful enough to move the rock from its original horizontal position.

4. The process of turning a sediment into a sedimentary rock.

5. (1) The Principle of Original Horizontality
   (2) The Principle of Superposition
   (3) The Principle of Lateral Continuity
   (4) The Principle of Cross-Cutting Relationships
   (5) The Principle of Fossil Succession
   (6) The Principle of Uniformitarianism

6. The Principle of Fossil Succession indicates the youngest rocks are on the bottom. Something disturbed the rock layers and flipped them over.

7. **False**. The area that is now the Grand Canyon was once under lots of water, and the sediments that settled out of the water formed the layers we can now see on the canyon walls.

8. The Principle of Lateral Continuity.

9. The Principle of Uniformitarianism. We know marine animals live in the sea today. We assume they also did so in the past.

Quiz 3

1. A mineral is an inorganic solid found in nature. It has a unique chemical composition and crystal structure.

2. No, because amber is organic and amorphous.

3. Quartz will scratch calcite because it is harder than calcite, but calcite won't scratch quartz. Calcite will scratch gypsum, however, because gypsum is softer than calcite. Other minerals are tested for their hardness relative to the minerals on the scale or relative to other items of known hardness, such as a fingernail, a penny, or a steel knife.

4. Yes, but only for certain minerals, because often specimens of the same mineral occur in different colors.

5. Crystalline solids are made up of atoms bonded in a three-dimensional geometric pattern.

6. Polymorphs are minerals with the same chemical formula but different crystal structures, such as diamond and graphite.

7. (1) HARDNESS – the ability to resist abrasion

   (2) CLEAVAGE – the way crystalline minerals split or break along planar surfaces

   (3) FRACTURE – the way minerals break along uneven surfaces

   (4) LUSTER – the way minerals reflect light

   (5) COLOR – specimens of the same mineral are often (but not always) different

8. Silicon, oxygen.

Quiz 4

1. Concordant plutons lie parallel to the pre-existing country rock. Discordant plutons cut across the country rock.

2. No, plutonic rocks are coarse-grained.

Asses, fools, dolts, chaff and bran, chaff and bran; porridge after meat.

— *Troilus and Cressida*

3. Felsic, intermediate, mafic, and ultramafic.

4. Magma is molten rock. Once the magma shoots out of a volcano or oozes out of a crack of some sort, it's called lava.

5. **False**. Batholiths must be at least 100 square kilometers in area. You could build a city on a batholith

6. **False**. Felsic and ultramafic magma are composed of pretty much the same elements but in different proportions.

7. No, volcanic rocks are fine-grained.

8. In every step of the continuous branch, the magma is forming plagioclase—just one mineral. The discontinuous branch forms four different minerals: olivine, pyroxene, amphibole, and biotite mica.

9. When different rock types come out of one type of magma.

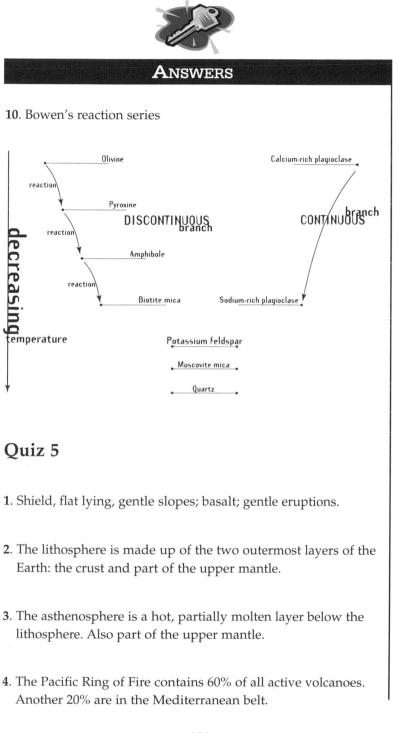

10. Bowen's reaction series

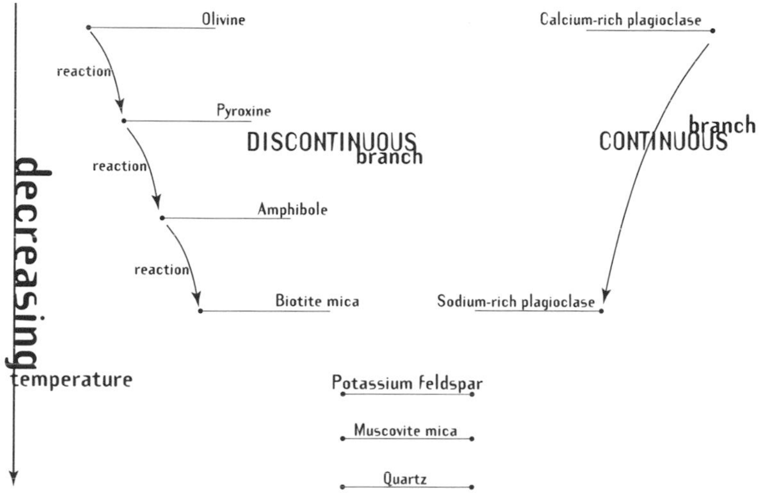

Quiz 5

1. Shield, flat lying, gentle slopes; basalt; gentle eruptions.

2. The lithosphere is made up of the two outermost layers of the Earth: the crust and part of the upper mantle.

3. The asthenosphere is a hot, partially molten layer below the lithosphere. Also part of the upper mantle.

4. The Pacific Ring of Fire contains 60% of all active volcanoes. Another 20% are in the Mediterranean belt.

5. In the lithosphere.

6. Edge.

7. Composite. Cinder Cones never get much bigger than 400 meters.

8. Fissure eruptions ooze lava that is so runny that it never forms a volcanic edifice. The magma is mafic and forms basalt.

Quiz 6

1. Water and freezing temperatures.

2. Thermal expansion and contraction.

3. Dissolution, oxidation, and hydrolysis.

4. Mechanical and chemical.

5. Weathering is faster at higher temperatures in hotter climates.

6. The breakdown of minerals into their component elements.

7. Gravity.

8. **False**. Mechanical weathering ONLY breaks rocks up into smaller pieces.

9. Weathering, transportation, and deposition.

10. Wind, water, and ice.

Quiz 7

1. Beach.

2. Shallow marine and desert; shallow marine.

3. The rock's visible shape, texture, and internal components that can be attributed to the environment in which it was formed are its "facies." For example, wind, which is a physical force, may form crossbeds.

4. Grain size.

5. Transgression.

6. Yes, by the processes of erosion and lithification.

7. Limestone, chert, salt (halite), gypsum, or evaporite.

8. Biochemical sedimentary rock made from the remains of plants.

9. Away from the land.

10. Self test. See Section D to check yourself.

Quiz 8

1. The reactions are faster at higher temperatures.

2. Yes. They can be part of the rock cycle. The metamorphic rock can undergo erosion and the clastic fragments can be lithified into a sedimentary rock.

3. Water and carbon dioxide.

4. Recrystallization.

Quiz 9

1. Foliation is a fabric or pattern that forms when minerals align themselves in flat or wavy parallel planes.

2. Contact and regional.

3. Country rock.

4. **a.** Slaty cleavage, which means it can easily split along cleavage planes, and the planes often have bumpy parallel ridges.

   b. Schistosity, which is scaly foliation composed of large-grained minerals you can see without magnifying them.

   c. Gneissosity, the coarsest foliation, which is characterized by alternating bands of light and dark minerals.

5. This was once at a tectonic plate boundary a long time ago. The Principle of Uniformitarianism.

6. No. This principle applies to sedimentary rocks. Contact metamorphic rocks will cross-cut the surrounding sedimentary layers. (Igneous rocks may be small intrusions or lava flows and also do not follow the principle.)

Quiz 10

1. Stress is a force applied to rock. Strain is the deformation or shape-change of the rock that results from the application of force.

2. They use strike and dip symbols. Strike is the direction or trend of the rock; dip is the tilt in degrees from the horizontal.

3. Uplift by folding, faulting, volcanism, or other ways.

4. **False**. Folds form beneath the surface of the Earth where rocks deform rather than fracturing in a brittle manner.

5. A mountain-building event.

6. No. Folds are only formed by compressional forces.

7. A mountain is an area of land that stands significantly higher than the land around it. Mountains come in a variety of sizes and shapes due to different processes of formation.

8. Fold; A; older.

9. Structural geology.

Quiz 11

1. Both forces form faults.

2. Dip-slip and strike-slip.

ANSWERS

3. **a.** The Himalayas and the Pacific Ring of Fire

   b. Mainly folding and faulting (Himalayas) and mainly volcanic (Ring of Fire).

You're never too old to do goofy stuff.

— Ward Cleaver

4. Strike-slip; California.

5. Joints are fractures where no movement takes place between the two separated sections of rock. Faults are fractures in which the two separated sections of rock move past and scrape against each other.

6. **False**. Mountains can be formed from faulting in both tensional and compressional geological environments.

7. Tensional; down.

8. Coarse; underground; Sierra Nevada.

9.

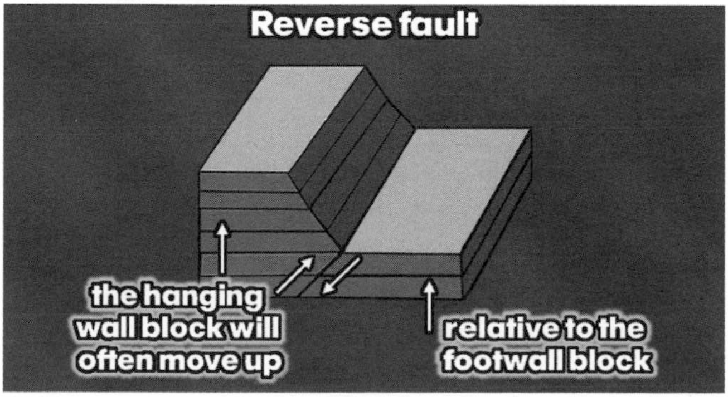
Reverse fault
the hanging wall block will often move up
relative to the footwall block

Quiz 12

1. Inner Core

   Outer Core

   Lower Mantle

   Transition zone

   Upper Mantle

   Upper mantle - partially molten zone - the asthenosphere

   Upper mantle - part of the lithosphere

   Crust - part of the lithosphere

2. S-waves are not transmitted; P-waves slow down.

3. No. The modified Mercalli scale only measures damage to humans and property. Neither were around during the Paleozoic.

4. P-waves. They expand and contract the material they're traveling through with a push-pull motion.

5. The Moho (the Mohorovicic discontinuity).

6. Rayleigh waves, or R-waves, ripple along the surface of the Earth, rolling forward in an elliptical (oval-shaped) path. Love waves, or L-waves, move the ground in a horizontal side-to-side-motion.

7.

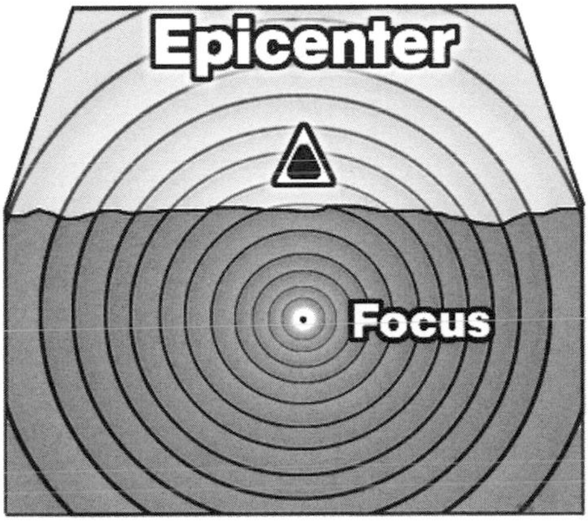

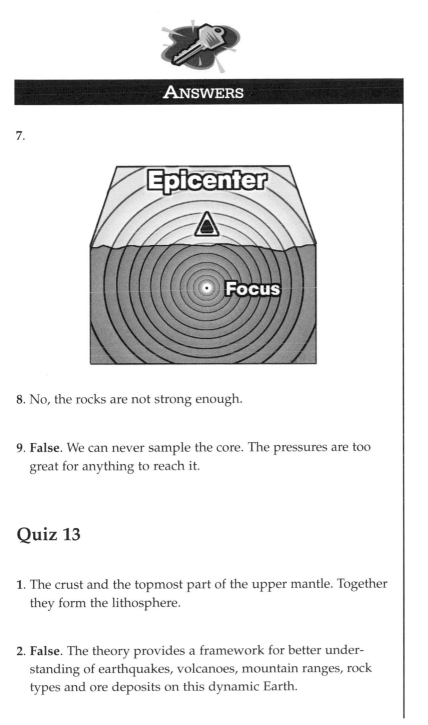

8. No, the rocks are not strong enough.

9. **False**. We can never sample the core. The pressures are too great for anything to reach it.

Quiz 13

1. The crust and the topmost part of the upper mantle. Together they form the lithosphere.

2. **False**. The theory provides a framework for better understanding of earthquakes, volcanoes, mountain ranges, rock types and ore deposits on this dynamic Earth.

3. Asthenosphere; pliable.

4. Divergent; oceanic; mafic.

5. The extrusion of lava creating new sea floor pushing old sea floor to the sides.

6. Plate tectonic theory provides a mechanism, and includes both oceanic and continental crust as moving plates.

7. Pangea.

8. **False**. These Continents were once one landmass.

9. **False.** S-waves slow down but do not stop in the asthenosphere.

10. Mid-Atlantic-Ridge; Andes or Japan or Himalayas; San Andreas. (Plus many more!)

Quiz 14

1. **a.** dissolved load: material (ions) that dissolved into the stream water.

b. suspended load: little particles that ride along in the current.

ANSWERS

c. bed load: larger material that travels along the bottom of the channel.

2. True. A stream deposits material along its channel. This material is often called a bar.

3.

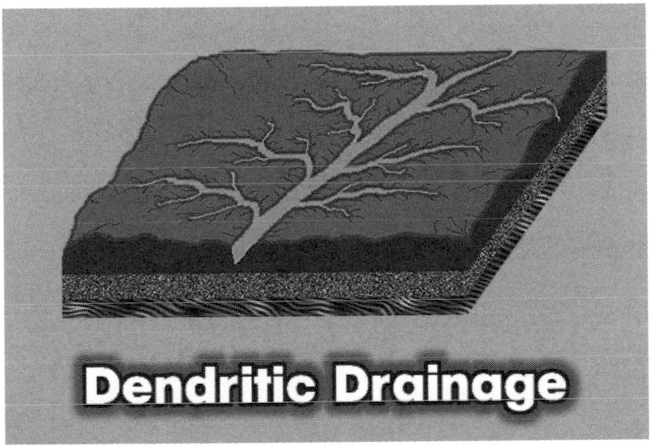

4. Stream piracy. Eroding upstream and gaining the headwaters of another stream.

5. A stream is any water flowing in a channel.

6. V-shaped.

7. When the stream alters its channel by cutting off a meander and flowing straight to its next curve. The meander is cutoff. The abandoned bend becomes a little, crescent-shaped lake called an oxbow lake.

8. **False**. Drainage basins can be anywhere from smaller than a square mile to the size of half of the USA, depending on the stream system we are describing.

9. Distributaries carry water away from a main channel by forming many smaller channels. Tributaries add water to the main channel.

10. The hydrologic cycle.

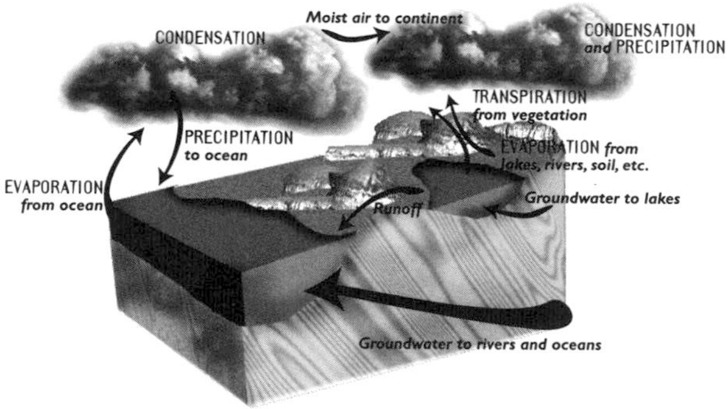

Quiz 15

1. As a wave approaches the shore, the bottom of the wave is slowed by friction where it meets the sea floor, the top continues to move in its orbital path and overtakes the base of the wave, forming a crest and then a crashing wave.

2. Sand grains carried along the shoreline by a current moving parallel to the beach.

3. By increasing the distance over which the wind blows, the length of time the wind blows, or the strength of the wind.

4. Breaker; swash; backwash.

5.

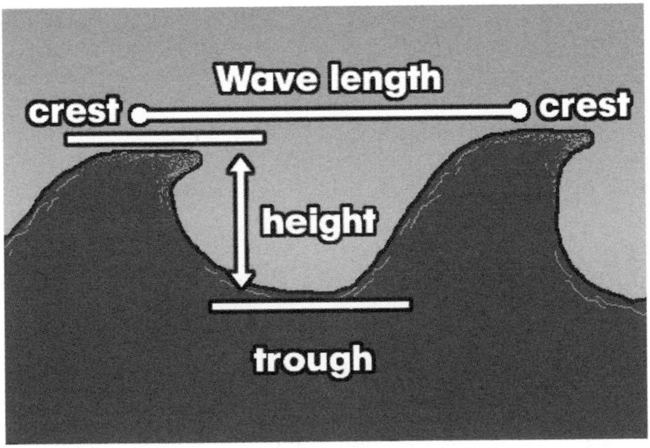

6. In the winter, waves pull the sand off the beach and form offshore sandbars. In the summer, waves carry the sand from the offshore sandbars back to the beach.

7. No. The beach has sand-sized grains. The finer material is washed away. Waves crashing on the beach destroy shells, and delicate life would not be preserved as fossils.

8. Barrier island.

9. Shorelines extend from the point where the water gets lowest at low tide, to the point where the waves lap the highest during a storm.

Quiz 16

1. **a.** Accumulation is the amount of snow added to a glacier annually.

   b. Ablation is the total amount of ice a glacier loses annually.

2. An ice cap is like a continental glacier, but it is smaller than 19,500 square miles.

3. **True**. The pressure from the upper ice can push the lower ice uphill.

4. Glacial ice, 10% ; snow, 80%.

5. Striations are grooves in the bedrock made when a glacier drags rocks along beneath it. These rocks scratch and gouge striations into the bedrock.

6. U-shaped.

7. **False**. The front of the glacier is disappearing at the same rate that the glacier is moving, so the glacier doesn't look like it's moving.

8. **False**. Two continental glaciers exist currently: one in Greenland and one in Antarctica.

9. A single mountain peak with cirques on at least three of its sides.

10. An elevated valley formed by tributary glaciers.

Practice Exam 1

1. (A) Cenozoic, Mesozoic, Paleozoic.

2. (C) Absolute time and relative time.

3. (C) Relative dating.

4. (D) Lateral continuity.

5. (E) Flat-lying sedimentary rocks.

You three-inch fool!

— *The Taming of the Shrew*

6. (E) All of the above.

7. (B) Oxygen and silicon are the most abundant minerals in the crust.

8. (D) Diamond and talc.

9. (C) A plane of weak bonds in the mineral.

10. (A) Ferromagnesian mineral.

11. (D) Rapidly, at the surface of.

12. (B) Concordant tabular bodies.

13. (B) How felsic magmas can be formed from mafic magma.

14. (E) Breaks the rock into smaller pieces.

15. (E) Lithification, compaction, cementation.

16. (D) That the ocean is moving off the land.

17. (B) Clastic and chemical.

Practice Exam 2

1. (C) Convergent, divergent, and transform.

2. (E) The drift of the continents was affected by the moon.

3. (D) The same structure trends.

4. (E) Divergent plate boundaries.

5. (C) The Circum-Pacific Belt.

6. (D) Perpendicular, solids.

7. (B) Primary and secondary waves.

8. (B) False.

9. (D) Outer core.

11. (B) Crust.

Word Scramble Solution

PETER PIPER PICKED A PECK OF PICKLED PLUTONS.

Eartho Crosso Solution

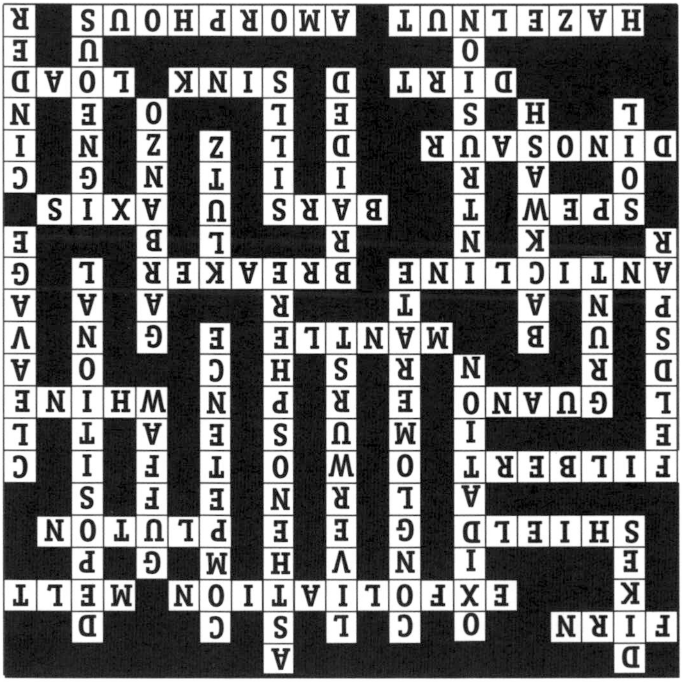

GLOSSARY

aa – Mafic lava flow with a rough, jagged surface.

ablation – The total amount of ice a glacier loses annually.

absolute dating – The numerical age of a geological feature or event (given in years).

accumulation – The amount of snow added to a glacier annually.

alluvial fan – An open, fan-shaped deposit of loose rock material at the place where a narrow mountain canyon opens onto a wide, flat plain.

amber – Fossilized tree sap. It is not a mineral because it is amorphous (has no crystal structure).

amorphous – Lacking an ordered crystal structure; without form.

amphibole – A common rock-forming silicate. Amphibole is often dark in color and is #6 on the Mohs scale of hardness. It has a variable chemical composition of calcium, iron, magnesium, silicon, oxygen, and many others.

anticline – A convex, upward fold. When eroded, the center beds (axis beds) are older than the beds on either side.

Archean – Old or ancient rocks from 3800–2500 million years ago.

ash (volcanic) – Fine, pyroclastic material less than 2 millimeters in size.

asthenosphere – A layer in the upper mantle where the rocks are close to their melting point and may be partially molten. The velocity of P- and S-waves slows down in this layer. The asthenosphere is the layer over which the plates of the lithosphere move.

atom – The smallest particle of an element that retains the properties of that element.

aureole – The zone adjacent to an igneous intrusion which shows the effect of contact metamorphism.

avalanche – A large mass of snow, ice, rock, and soil moving rapidly downhill under the effect of gravity.

axial plane – Plane passing through a series of hinge-lines or axes of a fold.

axis – A line dividing the fold; the hinge-line of a fold.

backwash (waves) – The water returning to the sea after a wave has broken onto the shore.

backwash (drinks) – The disgusting spitty stuff left in the bottom of the bottle.

barrier island – A significant offshore deposit of sand above sea-level. The Outer Banks of North Carolina are barrier islands.

bars (stream) – An accumulation of sand or gravel where the velocity of the stream has decreased.

basalt – A fine-grained, extrusive or volcanic, mafic igneous rock. Composed mostly of pyroxene and plagioclase, with some olivine or amphibole.

basaltic magma – See **mafic magma**.

basalt plateau – A large area built up by successive basaltic lava flows; can be thousands of feet thick.

Glossary

basin – A depressed area with no outlet.

batholith – A large, discordant igneous intrusion greater than 100 square kilometers (36 square miles).

beach – A shoreline made up of sand and pebbles.

beach environments – The area of the beach between low and high tides.

bed – The smallest easily recognizable unit in a sequence of rocks. They may be from a few inches to over 100 feet thick.

bedding – The layers of beds.

bedding planes – The planes that separate the beds.

bed load – The sediment moving along the bottom of the stream, neither in solution nor suspension; the coarsest sediment the stream carries.

biochemical sedimentary rock – Sedimentary rock that forms from organic sedimentation.

biotite mica – A common rock-forming silicate. Often dark in color and ranks #4 on the Mohs scale of hardness. It has a variable chemical composition of calcium, iron, magnesium, silicon, and oxygen with water in its crystal structure.

bipolar water molecule – Water molecules have a positively charged side and a negatively charged side, which accounts for many of the special properties of water. The weak charges on the molecule help break down minerals during chemical weathering.

body waves – Seismic waves (energy waves) that travel through the Earth.

bond (chemistry) – Binding mechanism between atoms.

Bond (espionage) – 007.

boulder – A clastic fragment larger than 256 millimeters (about 10 inches).

bottomset beds – See **delta**.

Bowen's reaction series – An interpretation of the crystallization sequence of minerals in igneous rocks, theorized by N. L. Bowen in 1936.

braided stream – A tangled network of small streams that split and reunite. The stream cannot carry all its load and has deposited the sediment in its channel.

braided writer – Igor Torgeson, Cerebellum's Head Comedy Writer.

breaker – Crashing wave close to the shore.

breccia – A clastic sedimentary rock composed of angular, large-sized fragments. Most are greater than 2 millimeters in size.

burial pressure (sediments) – See **compaction**.

calcite – A common rock-forming mineral. Calcite is an oxide, not a silicate, and ranks #3 on the Mohs scale of hardness. It has a chemical composition of calcium, carbon, and oxygen, and is known as calcium carbonate ($CaCO_3$). Calcite will react with weak hydrochloric acid to give off carbon dioxide as a gas. It fizzes.

calcium carbonate – See **calcite**.

Cambrian – A geological time period from 570 to 505 million years ago. Named after *Cambria*, the Latin name for Wales.

canyon – A deep, narrow, steep-sided valley which often has a stream at the base.

carbonate rock – See **limestone**.

Glossary

carbonic acid – A weak acid formed by the reaction of water and carbon dioxide in the atmosphere.

Carboniferous – The European name for the time period from 360 to 286 million years ago. This time period is equivalent to the Mississippian and Pennsylvanian periods in America.

cementation – The binding together of sedimentary particles.

Cenozoic – The geological era from 60 million years ago until today, known as the era of new or recent life.

chalk – A sedimentary rock formed by biological processes. It is mostly composed of the mineral calcite.

channel – A narrow depression that carries flowing water either continuously or periodically.

chemical composition – The chemical components of minerals or rocks, generally expressed as elements or oxides.

chemical compound – A material containing two or more elements.

chemical sedimentary rocks – Sedimentary rocks that form from precipitation of minerals from a solution.

chemical weathering – The decomposition of rocks at the Earth's surface by chemical reactions. Chemical weathering usually changes the minerals in the weathering rocks.

chemistry – The chemistry of a rock or mineral is its chemical composition.

cinder cones – Small, steep-sided volcano (usually less than 400 meters tall) made of pyroclastic materials.

cirque – Amphitheater-shaped hollows carved out of the sides of mountains by glacial processes.

clast – A clastic fragment.

clastic fragments – Solid rock and mineral fragments produced by weathering.

clastic sedimentary rocks – Rocks formed from clastic fragments.

clay-sized particle – Sedimentary fragment less than 1/256 millimeter (0.00016 inches) in size.

claystone – A clastic sedimentary rock composed of fragments less than 1/256 millimeter (0.00016 inches) in size.

clay mineral – Small, platy minerals that are often the end products of weathering.

cleavage (mineral) – The tendency of minerals to break or cleave along a plane which has low resistance due to the pattern of the mineral's crystal structure.

cleavage (rock) – The tendency of rocks to break or cleave along a plane due to the alignment of the minerals (foliation).

coal – A biochemical sedimentary rock formed from plant debris (peat).

cobble – A clastic fragment from 64 to 256 millimeters in size (about 2.5 - 10 inches).

color – The interaction of visible light with the surface of the mineral. Color is dependent on the chemical composition and the crystal structure of the mineral.

compaction – Decrease in the sediments' pore spaces as the grains are pushed closer together by weight from above.

competence – The ability of a stream to carry particles of various sizes.

composite volcano – Volcanoes composed of alternating pyroclastic rocks and lava flows. They are steeper near the summit than at their bases.

Glossary

concordant plutons – Igneous intrusions parallel to the country rock into which they intrude.

conglomerate – A clastic sedimentary rock composed of rounded, large-sized fragments, most of which are greater than 2 millimeters in size.

contact metamorphism – The change in texture and mineralogy of a rock due to heat from an igneous rock intrusion.

continental crust – The outermost layer of the Earth. It is composed largely of rocks which have the same composition as granite. The continental crust is an average of 35 kilometers thick, but can be 20-90 kilometers thick. The continental crust is light compared to the oceanic crust.

continental glacier – Huge, thick, slow-moving ice sheets that cover at least 50,000 square kilometers (19,500 square miles).

continental shelf – A continent that becomes sea floor, sloping gently into the ocean to a depth of about 200 meters, at which point the slope suddenly becomes much steeper.

continental slope – Ocean-covered area further seaward than the continental shelf. It is a marked increase in slope (about 3 to 6 degrees).

continuous branch – In Bowen's reaction series, the crystallization of the mineral plagioclase in a magma.

convergent plate boundary – Where two or more plates move towards each other.

core – The central part of the Earth, which extends from a depth of 2,900 kilometers (1,800 miles) to the center at 6000 kilometers (3700) miles. See also **inner core** and **outer core**.

country rock – The existing rock that predates the igneous intrusion or the metamorphism.

creep – The extremely-slow-yet-persistent movement of material downhill due to gravity.

crest – The top of a wave.

Cretaceous – The period lasting from 144 to 66 million years ago. The Cretaceous is the most recent period of the Mesozoic Era. Its name comes from the Latin word *creta* which means "chalk."

cross-bedding – Beds deposited on an inclined plane.

cross-cutting relationship – The principle stating that material that cuts into a bed of country rock is younger than the country rock.

crust – The outermost layer of the Earth; crust includes both continental crust and oceanic crust.

cutoff (stream) – A new, shorter channel cutting through the inside of a meander loop.

crystal – A mineral in which the crystal structure is outwardly expressed as a series of flat surfaces that form a specific shape.

crystal settling – In a melt, the sinking of crystals to the bottom of the magma chamber.

crystal structure – The regular arrangement of elements into a three-dimensional structure.

crystalline – Having the properties of a crystal.

crystallize – The formation of a solid from a liquid.

crystallization – The process by which a fluid becomes a crystalline solid.

crystallization temperature – The temperature at which a mineral will become a solid: generally between 1200 and 800 degrees Celsius.

Glossary

deep time – The billions of years that form the Earth's history.

delta – A triangular-shaped area at the mouth of a river; formed by the river depositing sediment it transports; composed of relatively flat-lying topset and bottomset beds with steeper, cross-bedded, foreset beds between.

deltaic environments – The area in or close to a delta.

dendritic drainage pattern – In a drainage basin, the streams branch randomly and resemble a tree's branches.

depositional basin – A depressed area with no outlet, into which sediment is being deposited: for example, an ocean basin.

desert – An area that receives less than 10 inches of rainfall annually.

desert environments – The area in or close to a desert.

Devonian – A period in the Paleozoic Era lasting from 408 to 360 million years ago. Named after Devon in England.

diamond – The hardest mineral known to humankind: a #10 on the Mohs scale of hardness. It is composed only of carbon, and its carbon atoms are packed closely together, since diamonds form under high pressure deep in the Earth's crust or upper mantle.

dike – A discordant, tabular igneous intrusion.

dinosaur – The "terrible lizard" which lived from the Triassic to the Cretaceous Periods. Luckily for us humans, they are extinct.

dip – The angle formed by the plane of a sedimentary bed (or fault) and a horizontal plane.

dip angle – The measurement of the angle of the dip. The dip angle will never be more than 90° unless the bed is overturned.

dip-slip faults – A fault in which one side moves up or down relative to the other side.

discharge (stream) – The rate of flow in a stream measured in volume and time (such as gallons per second).

discontinuous branch – In Bowen's reaction series, the crystallization of mafic minerals in a magma.

discordant plutons – Igneous intrusions that cut across the country rock into which they intrude.

dissolution – A type of chemical weathering in which the minerals break down into their component elements.

dissolved load – Material (ions) in solution that dissolved during chemical weathering.

distributaries (stream) – Smaller channels that split from a main stream and do not rejoin it. They are often found in a delta.

divergent plate boundary – The area where two or more tectonic plates are moving away from each other.

dome – A large, upwardly-arched area of land that results from an anticline.

downcutting (stream) – The ability of a river to cut downward vertically.

drainage basin – A specific area of land served by its own drainage system.

drainage system – The network of streams and lakes that drains a specific area.

earthquake – A large release in energy along a fault sending seismic waves throughout the Earth.

elastic rebound theory – Theory stating that under stress, rocks behave like rubber bands: they will expand until the stress becomes too great and they break.

element – A substance composed of just one type of atom.

environment – The temperature, precipitation, and other physical properties in a given area at a given time.
See **paleoenvironment**.

eon – The first and largest division of geological time. There are 4 eons: Pre-Archean (or Hadean), Archean, Proterozoic, and Phanerozoic.

epicenter – The point on the Earth's surface directly above the focus of an earthquake.

epoch – The fourth division of geological time; represents the subdivisions of a period.

era – The second division of geological time. Each era has at least two periods.

erode – To wear away the land.

erosion – The weathering and the transportation of weathered material; generally by wind, water, ice, and gravity.

evaporite – Sedimentary rock formed by the evaporation of seawater.

exfoliation – The mechanical weathering of rocks, in which rounded sheets of rock peel off rocks or outcrops the way layers peel off a big onion.

exfoliation dome – A rounded mountain formed by exfoliation.

extrusive igneous rock – Rocks formed from lava or pyroclastic material on the surface of the Earth. Also called volcanic igneous rock.

facies (sedimentary) – A sedimentary rock's physical, chemical and biological characteristics, which reflect the environment in which the rock was formed.

fault – A fracture in the Earth where the two separated sides move relative to each other.

fault plane – The actual site of a fracture in a fault.

faunal succession – Animals of a particular time in history. See **fossil succession**.

feldspar group – A group of minerals with similar chemical composition, including potassium-rich feldspar (orthoclase), and sodium-rich and calcium-rich feldspars known as plagioclase.

feldspar (potassium-rich) – A common rock-forming silicate. Potassium feldspar is often white or pink in color, but can also be green; is a #6 on the Mohs scale of hardness; and has a chemical composition of potassium, aluminum, silicon and oxygen.

felsic – An igneous rock, magma, or lava with a composition of more than 65% silica. Felsic rocks are usually light-colored. Felsic magma is very thick and viscous, moderately hot (approximately 900 Celsius), and will not flow far, if at all. This type of magma generally erupts explosively rather than forming lava flows.

felsic minerals – Quartz, potassium feldspar, and muscovite.

ferromagnesian minerals – Minerals rich in magnesium and iron. They are dark-colored, and include minerals such as pyroxene, amphibole, and biotite mica.

firn – Compacted snow.

fissure eruptions – Thin, runny basaltic lava flowing out along a long crack in the Earth. Forms a lava sheet rather than a flow.

flood plain (stream) – The area affected by a stream's flooding.

floral succession – The plants of a particular time. See **fossil succession** and **faunal succession**.

GLOSSARY

fluorite – A mineral which ranks #4 on the Mohs scale of hardness with a chemical composition of calcium and fluorine. It has excellent cleavage planes and often forms eight-sided, diamond-shaped crystals.

fluvial environment – The area in and around rivers.

focus – The place beneath the Earth's surface where an earthquake's rupture starts.

fold – A deformed rock bed produced by compressional, ductile deformation.

foliation – The alignment of platy or linear minerals in a flat or wavy plane, or along a line within a rock.

footwall block (fault) – The part of the rock under the fault plane.

foreset beds – See **delta**.

fossil – Any evidence of past life, such as remains or traces.

fossil succession – As their environment changes over time, animal and plant species change, too. Once a species has evolved or become extinct it cannot reappear in the geological record again.

fracture – The breaking of a mineral along any surface other than a cleavage plane. A fracture is much more uneven than a break along a cleavage plane.

freezing temperature – See **crystallization temperature.**

frost wedging – The mechanical weathering of rocks on the Earth's surface caused by water freezing and thawing.

fundamental principles – Main theories that serve as a basis for geological interpretation of the rock record.

galena – A mineral with a cubic crystal structure and the chemical composition of lead (Pb) and sulfur (S). Used as ore for lead.

geology – The study of the Earth.

geologic event – An important occurrence in the geological past that is recorded in the rocks. Also used to describe geological disasters today.

geologic record – The geological history of the Earth interpreted from the rocks.

geologic time – A very long time: thousands, millions and billions of years.

geologic time scale – A chronological series of events in the history of the Earth with given names for the various time units.

geologist – A person who studies the Earth.

glacial environment – The area in or close to a glacier.

glacier – A moving mass of ice.

glass – A material that cools very fast and does not develop a crystal structure.

gneiss – A metamorphic rock showing gneissosity.

gneissosity – Coarse-grained foliation. The individual mineral grains are separated into light and dark layers.

graded bedding – Bedding in which the size of the clastic sediments changes systematically (goes from large to small or from small to large) through the bed.

gradient – Steepness of a slope. It is calculated by dividing the vertical distance by the horizontal distance.

grain growth (metamorphic) – The nucleation and growth of a new mineral.

graphite – A soft mineral composed of carbon. Ranks #2 on the Mohs scale of hardness. Its atoms are loosely packed, so graphite flakes easily. Used as pencil lead.

Glossary

granite – Coarse-grained, intrusive or plutonic, felsic igneous rock. Composed mainly of quartz and potassium feldspar, with some muscovite mica and biotite mica.

granule – A clastic fragment between 2 and 4 millimeters in size (about $\frac{1}{6}$ to $\frac{1}{12}$ inch).

granular texture – See **hornfelsic texture**.

gravel – Sediment fragments larger than 2 millimeters.

groundmass – The fine-grained matrix in a porphyritic rock.

groundwater – Water in the fractures or small spaces between the grains of rock or soil.

gypsum – A mineral formed from the evaporation of seawater. It is a soft mineral which ranks a #2 on the Mohs scale of hardness. Its chemical composition is calcium and sulfur with water.

Hadean or Pre-Archean – Named for Hades, god of the underworld. This is the "hidden" period of geological time which has left little rock evidence.

halite – A mineral with a cubic crystal structure and the chemical composition of NaCl (known as good ol' table salt).

hanging valley – Elevated valley formed by tributary glaciers.

hanging wall (fault) – Mining term for the part of the rock above the fault plane.

hard hat – To be donned when you see "Watch for falling rocks." Note: May result in very bad case of hat hair.

hardness – A mineral's resistance to scratching. The Mohs scale of hardness measures the relative hardness of minerals.

headward erosion – The lengthening of a stream by erosion of the upland above the stream source.

heat – A form of energy produced by the rapid vibration of atoms.

height (wave) – Distance from crest to trough.

hematite – Mineral that can be reddish-brown with an earthy luster, or silvery with a metallic luster. It is an oxide (not a silicate) composed of iron and oxygen, and gives the red color we see in many rocks.

Hershdemirmir – A king of Siamese cats. Born April 7, 1983, died November 12, 1990.

historical geology – The study of the formation and evolution of the Earth, and life on Earth.

horn (glacial) – A single mountain that has cirques on at least three of its sides.

hornfels – A metamorphic rock with a hornfelsic texture.

hornfelsic texture (metamorphic) – The study of the formation and evolution of the Earth, and life on the Earth.

hydrologic cycle – Texture in which a rock's minerals are oriented randomly. There is no foliation.

hydrologic cycle – The cycle of water in, on, and above the Earth.

hydrolysis – Chemical weathering which involves the dissolution of water (H_2O) into a hydrogen ion ($H+$) and a hydroxyl ion ($OH-$). The $H+$ replaces the positive ions in the mineral and the $OH-$ ion is left behind in the solution.

ice cap – Glacier that looks and flows like a continental glacier, but is smaller than 19,500 square miles.

igneous rock – Rock formed from magma or lava. Named after the Latin word *ignis,* which means fire.

inner core – The central part of the Earth from a depth of 5,100 kilometers (3,200 miles) to the center of the Earth at 6000 kilometers (3700 miles). Believed to be solid iron and nickel.

Glossary

inorganic – Not formed by life processes.

intensity (earthquake) – How much damage an earthquake causes as measured on the modified Mercalli scale.

intermediate – An igneous rock, magma, or lava with a composition between that of felsic and mafic: 53-65% silica. Intermediate magma/lava is moderately hot (approximately 1000 Celsius) and is viscous rather than runny, so it will not flow far.

intrusive igneous rock – Rocks formed from magma within the Earth. Also called plutonic igneous rock.

ions – An electrically charged atom or group of atoms that get their charge from the addition or loss of one or more electrons.

ions (uncoordinated) – Ions that are in random orientation rather than in a definite orientation or structure.

isomorphs – Minerals with the same crystal structure but different chemical compositions.

joint – A fracture in the Earth in which the two sides do not move. A brittle deformation of the rock.

Jurassic – The middle period in the Mesozoic Era, from 208 to 144 million years ago. Named after the Jura Mountains in France.

kaolinite – A clay mineral often formed from the hydrolysis of feldspar. Used to make fine china and also to whiten paper.

lacustrine environment – The area in or close to a lake or lagoon.

lagoon – A shallow lake or pond, usually with no strong currents.

landslide – A mass of loosened soil and rock that slides down a hill.

Pesto is the quiche of the 80's.

– When Harry Met Sally

lateral continuity – The fundamental geologic principle that sediments are deposited in layers that extend horizontally in all directions.

lateral erosion – The wearing away of the sides of a stream. The stream undercuts the sides below the water level, and mass wasting and erosion occurs above the water level.

lava – Magma that reaches the Earth's surface.

limestone – A sedimentary rock formed by either chemical precipitation (chemical sedimentary rock) or biological processes (biochemical sedimentary rock). Predominantly composed of the mineral calcite.

limonite – A yellow-brown iron oxide.

littoral environment – See **shallow marine environment**.

lithification – The combination of processes that make a sediment into a rock. From the Greek *lithos*, or stone.

lithify – To make into a rock.

lithosphere – The area composed of the crust and the topmost part of the upper mantle. The lithosphere is the outer ridged layer that we divide into the Earth's tectonic plates.

load – All the material a stream carries.

longshore current – A current that runs parallel to the shoreline.

longshore drift – Sand grains carried along the shore by the longshore current.

lounge – To loll, idle, or pass time in a relaxed way. The summit of style and space-age groovin'.

Love waves – Surface waves (seismic waves or energy waves) released by an earthquake. L-waves travel along the surface of the Earth in a serpentine path and cause much damage.

low velocity zone – See **asthenosphere**.

luster – The reflection of light off the surface of a mineral.

mafic – An igneous rock, a magma, or a lava which contains 45-52% silica and is rich in magnesium (Mg) and iron (Fe). Mafic magma and lava is hot (approximately 1200 degrees Celsius) and runny, so it can flow long distances. Mafic minerals, including pyroxene, amphibole, and biotite mica, are dark in color.

magma – Molten rock that may contain gas and solid mineral crystals.

magma chamber – A reservoir of magma within the crust.

magmatic differentiation – The process of developing more than one magma type from a single parent magma.

magnitude (earthquake) – Measures the amount of energy released by an earthquake. See **Richter scale**.

mantle – The central part of the Earth's layers from the core at a depth of 2,900 km (1,800 miles) to the crust at 20 to 90 km. Believed to be ultramafic in composition. Consists of the lower mantle, the transition zone, the asthenosphere, and the upper mantle.

marine – Area relating to the sea or ocean.

marine regression – The withdrawal of the sea exposing more land.

marine transgression – The invasion of the sea so it covers more land.

mass wasting – The downhill movement of material due to gravity. Also called "mass movement."

meander – One of a series of loops in the course of a stream.

mechanical weathering – See **physical weathering**.

melt – Magma.

Mesozoic – "Middle life." The geological era from 245 to 60 million years ago.

metallic luster – A mineral that reflects light like a metal. Includes brassy, coppery, silvery, and golden luster.

metamorphic rocks – Rocks that have been changed due to heat, pressure, fluids, chemical reactions, or any combination of these factors.

metamorphose – To change form.

metamorphosed rocks – Rocks that have changed in texture, mineralogy, composition, or any combination of these characteristics.

mica – A group of minerals that have a platy crystal structure and usually break easily into layers.

Mid-Atlantic Ridge – The mid-oceanic ridge of the Atlantic Ocean.

mid-oceanic ridge – A continuous mountain ridge that occurs in most oceans (not always the middle). Mafic rocks are produced at these divergent plate margins.

migrating fluids – Iron-rich fluids that move within the Earth.

mineral – An inorganic solid found in nature which has a unique chemical composition and crystal structure.

mineral assemblage – The minerals that make up a rock.

mineralogy – The study of the minerals that make up a rock.

Mississippian – A period in the Paleozoic Era that lasted from 360-320 million years ago. Named after the state of Mississippi.

GLOSSARY

Mister Seventies – Writer also known as the Non-Answer Man. A Cerebellum phenomenon that flourishes when a radio man, a professor, and an answer man are all shoehorned into a small space.

modified Mercalli scale – Scale that measures the intensity of an earthquake by assessing how much damage the earthquake causes.

Mohorovicic discontinuity (Moho) – The area between the crust and the upper mantle where P-waves increase in velocity.

mountain – Land that stands significantly higher than its surroundings.

mud cracks – Cracks that form when clay-rich sediment dries out. Can be preserved in sedimentary rocks.

mudslide – The sliding of a mass of loosened, saturated soil down a hill.

mudstone – A clastic sedimentary rock composed of fragments under $\frac{1}{16}$ millimeter in size.

muscovite mica – A common rock-forming silicate. Muscovite is often colorless and ranks #4 on the Mohs scale of hardness. It has a variable chemical composition of potassium, magnesium, silicon, and oxygen with water in its crystal structure.

non-metallic luster – The way a mineral reflects the light. Lusters may be earthy, waxy, glassy, or pearly.

non-plunging fold – A fold with a horizontal axis.

normal fault – A dip-slip fault in which the hanging wall block of the fault moves up relative to the footwall block.

nuée ardente – A "glowing cloud" of pyroclastic material that rushes down the side of a volcano at a speed of up to 100 miles per hour.

oblique-slip fault – A fault that combines dip-slip and strike-slip movement.

obsidian – Volcanic glass.

oceanic crust – The outermost layer of the Earth. Made up of rocks composed of basalt. It is an average of 5-10 kilometers thick and its density is 3.0 grams/square centimeter. The oceanic crust is heavy in comparison with the continental crust.

olivine – A common rock-forming silicate. Olivine is often apple-green in color and ranks #8 on the Mohs scale of hardness. It has a variable chemical composition of iron, magnesium, silicon, and oxygen.

Ordovician – A period in the Paleozoic Era, lasting from 505-438 million years ago. Named after an ancient Celtic tribe from Wales.

original horizontality – Fundamental geologic principle that states that sedimentary beds are usually deposited in flat layers. If they are tilted, some geological event must have occurred to move the rocks.

orogenesis – Mountain building.

outer core – The outer part of the Earth's core, from a depth of 2,900 kilometers (1,800 miles) to 5,100 kilometers (3,200 miles). Believed to be made of molten iron and nickel.

oxbow lake – The curved lake formed by the cutoff of a meander.

oxbow scar – The filled-in curved lake formed by the cutoff of a meander.

oxidation – In chemical weathering, oxidation is a reaction involving the addition of oxygen.

Pacific "Ring of Fire" – A zone of high volcanic activity (and earthquakes) that surrounds the Pacific Ocean.

GLOSSARY

pahoehoe – Mafic lava flow with a ropy surface.

paleoenvironment – The temperature, precipitation, and other physical properties in a given area at a given time in the past. See **environment**.

Paleozoic – "Old life." The geological era from 570 - 245 million years ago.

Pangea – "All land." Wegner's name for the land when all the continents were joined in one giant landmass.

peat – A biochemical sediment formed from plant and animal remains.

pebble – A clastic fragment between 4 and 64 millimeters in size (about 1/6 - 2.5 inches).

pelagic environment – The deep, open ocean environment.

Pennsylvanian – A period in the Paleozoic Era, lasting from 320-286 million years ago. Named after the state of Pennsylvania.

period – The third subdivision of geological time.

Permian – The youngest period in the Paleozoic Era, lasting from 286-245 million years ago. Named after an area in Russia called the Perm.

Phanerozoic eon – The youngest eon, lasting from 570 million years ago until today. Means "abundant life."

phenocrysts – The large crystals in a porphyritic rock.

physical geology – The study of the processes involved in the inorganic (material) evolution of the Earth.

physical properties (minerals) – The properties of minerals we can see, test for, and measure.

physical weathering – Weathering that breaks rocks into smaller and smaller pieces without changing their mineralogy or chemical composition.

plagioclase (calcium and sodium-rich) – A common rock-forming silicate which is part of the feldspar group. Plagioclase is often white or gray in color. It ranks #6 on the Mohs scale of hardness, and has a chemical composition of sodium, calcium, aluminum, silicon, and oxygen.

plate boundary – The area where two plates meet.

plate margins – The edges of the plates.

plates – Large segments including the oceanic and continental crust, and the uppermost mantle, which move relative to each other.

plate tectonic theory – The theory that the upper, brittle plates of the lithosphere move on the ductile asthenosphere by sea-floor spreading.

plunging fold – Fold whose axis is not horizontal and appears to dip or plunge into the surrounding rock and soil.

plutonic igneous rock – Rock formed from magma within the Earth. Also called intrusive igneous rock. Named after Pluto, the Roman God of the underworld.

pluton – Body of intrusive igneous rock.

polymorphs – Minerals with the same chemical composition but different crystal structures.

porphyry – A rock with porphyritic texture.

porphyritic texture – An igneous texture characterized by larger crystals, called phenocrysts, surrounded by a fine-grained matrix of little crystals.

Glossary

pork arthritic texture – The gnarled and knobby feel of an old pig's posterior.

Pre-Archean (Hadean) – The first (oldest) eon, lasting from 4600 to 3800 million years ago. Pre-Archean means "before the ancient rocks." Also called the Hadean Eon, for Hades the Greek god of the underworld. We have only found a few examples of rocks from this age.

Precambrian – All rocks older than the Cambrian Period (older than 570 million years). Includes rocks from the three earliest eons.

precipitation – Snow, rain, and hail.

pressure – A force expressed in weight per area. Used in geology to refer to the pressure exerted on buried rocks.

primordial – The beginning; most primitive; first created.

Proterozoic – The eon lasting from 2500 to 570 million years ago. Means "former life."

pumice – A volcanic glass full of bubbles left by volcanic gasses.

P-waves (Primary waves) – Body waves (seismic waves or energy waves) an earthquake releases; P-waves travel through the Earth and are the first to arrive at the seismograph station. They travel the fastest of all the seismic waves: 6 to 14 kilometers per second.

pyrite – A hard mineral which ranks #6 on the Mohs scale of hardness. Has a chemical composition of iron and sulfur. Pyrite is not gold, as any fool knows. It looks like gold, but is much harder and has a lower density.

pyroclastic material – "Fire fragments." The solid pieces of igneous material that are expelled (often violently) from a volcano.

pyroxene – A common rock-forming silicate. Pyroxene is often dark in color and ranks #6 on the Mohs scale of hardness. It has a variable chemical composition of calcium, iron, magnesium, silicon, oxygen, and many other elements.

quartz – The hardest common rock-forming mineral, it ranks #7 on the Mohs scale of hardness and has a chemical composition of pure silica. The atoms are packed in a three-dimensional structure of silica tetrahedra quartz. It is very resistant to erosion and is in many sedimentary and metamorphic rocks.

Quaternary – The second period of the Tertiary Era, lasting from 1.6 million years ago until present. It was named a long time ago when geologic time was divided in four: primary (before life); secondary (old, unusual life); Tertiary (life close to today); and Quaternary (life like today).

quenched – Cooled very quickly.

radial drainage system – Drainage system in which all the streams flow outward from a central upland area.

radiometric dating – Absolute dating technique that uses radioactive isotopes to find a numerical age of a rock or geological event.

rain water – Naturally acidic precipitation. Rain has a pH of 5.6 due to the reaction of water and carbon dioxide in the atmosphere, producing weak carbonic acid.

ratheskeller – A restaurant modeled after a German city hall; specialty is serving beer.

Rayleigh waves – Surface waves (seismic waves or energy waves) released by an earthquake. Rayleigh waves travel along the surface of the Earth like ocean waves and cause much damage.

reaction rim – One mineral surrounding or rimming a core that consists of another mineral. A reaction caught in the middle of the process.

recrystallization – A metamorphic rock that forms into a new mineral with a different crystal structure.

rectangular drainage system – Drainage pattern in which streams follow joints and faults, forming a rectangular, criss-cross pattern.

regional metamorphism – Large-scale metamorphism due to heat, pressure, and fluids. Usually associated with convergent plate margins.

relative dating – The chronological ordering of geological features or events without assigning a numerical age.

reverse fault – A dip-slip fault in which the hanging wall block of the fault moves down relative to the footwall block. The fault plane is usually greater than 45°.

Richter scale – A logarithmic scale which assigns a numerical measurement to the amount of energy, known as the magnitude, that an earthquake releases.

river – See **stream**.

ripplemarks – Ripples preserved in a sedimentary rock.

rock – An aggregate of one or more minerals. Will get you arrested if you throw it through the window of a government building.

rock fall – Rocks loosened by physical and chemical weathering that fall down a steep mountainside.

rock formation – A body of rock identifiable by its physical characteristics and its place on the geological time scale.

rock cycle – The interrelationship of igneous, metamorphic, and sedimentary rocks.

runoff – Water flowing on the surface of the Earth.

saltation – The intermittent movement of the bed load in a stream.

sand – Sedimentary fragment between $\frac{1}{16}$ and 2 millimeters in size.

sand bar (ocean) – An offshore deposit of sand. May or may not be above water level.

sandstone – A clastic sedimentary rock composed of fragments between $\frac{1}{16}$ and 2 millimeters in size.

schist – A metamorphic rock showing schistosity.

schistosity (schistose foliation) – Coarse-grained metamorphic foliation with individual mineral grains that are large enough to see with the naked eye.

sea-floor spreading – Theory developed in 1950 by Harry Hess. Explains the spreading of the ocean floor away from the mid-oceanic ridges; the driving mechanism for plate tectonics.

sediment – Solid fragments resulting from the weathering of rocks. They have been transported by wind, water, and ice, and are usually unconsolidated or loose.

sedimentary rocks – Rocks formed from sediment by lithification, compaction, and cementation.

seismic waves – Energy waves released by an earthquake.

seismograph – Device which records an earthquake's seismic waves.

shale – A clastic sedimentary rock composed of fragments smaller than $\frac{1}{16}$ millimeter in size.

shallow marine environments – The area in or close to the shoreline. Usually the area of the continental shelf.

shield volcano – Volcano formed from hot, runny mafic magma that erupts relatively quietly and forms the volcano's gently dipping sides.

shorelines – Areas where water meets land. Includes the area ranging from high to low tide.

silica – A chemical compound of silicon and oxygen.

silicate – The most common rock-forming minerals built up of silica tetrahedra. The silicate ion is a four-faced pyramid composed of one silicon atom surrounded by four oxygen atoms.

silica tetrahedra – A four-faced, pyramidic molecule composed of one silicon atom surrounded by four oxygen atoms.

siliceous – Rich in silica.

sill – A tabular igneous intrusion which lies parallel (concordant) to the country rock.

silt – Sedimentary fragment between $\frac{1}{16}$ and $\frac{1}{256}$ millimeter in size.

siltstone – A clastic sedimentary rock composed of fragments between $\frac{1}{16}$ and $\frac{1}{256}$ millimeter in size.

Silurian – A period in the Paleozoic Era that lasted from 438 until 408 million years ago. Named after a Celtic tribe in Wales.

slate – A fine-grained metamorphic rock that breaks or cleaves along a plane due to the alignment of its minerals (foliation).

slaty cleavage – Fine-grained foliation with tiny grains that you cannot see without magnifying.

solid – One of the three states of matter (the other two are liquid and gas). A solid's atoms are tightly held together by bonds.

solifluction – Mass wasting of the saturated upper layer of the ground in cold climates. An erosion process aided by freezing and thawing water.

spit – An elongated deposit of sand formed across an inlet due to longshore drift. Looks like a small addition to the beach.

stock – A discordant pluton smaller than 100 square kilometers.

strain – A change in shape due to stress.

strata – Layers of rock.

stratification – The formation, accumulation, or deposition of layers of rock.

stratovolcano – See **composite volcano**.

stream – Water flowing in a channel. Any size.

stream piracy – The diversion of water from one stream into one that is lengthening due to headward erosion. (Aarrr.)

stress – Directed pressure. A force applied to rocks.

striations – Scratches in the rock made by a glacier as it drags rocks along beneath it.

strike – The direction of the line formed where a tilted bed of rock meets an imaginary horizontal plane.

strike-slip fault – Fault in which the separated sections slide laterally (sideways) past each other.

structural geology – The study of folds and faults.

structure (crystal) – See **crystal structure**.

structure (rock) – The physical form of a rock, including features such as joints, fractures, grain size, and cementation.

subduction – One plate moving beneath another.

superposition or **superimposition** – An older stream pattern superimposed on more recently exposed rocks. The stream erodes the more recently exposed rocks, maintaining its existing path.

superposition – Fundamental geological principle stating that the oldest sedimentary beds are on the bottom of a sedimentary sequence.

surface waves – Seismic waves (energy waves) an earthquake releases along the surface of the Earth.

suspended load – The fine particles (clay and silt) that are carried along by a stream's current.

swash – The water that rushes up on the shore following the crash of a breaker.

swashbuckler – A flashy, sword-wielding adventurer.

S-waves (Secondary waves) – Body waves (seismic waves or energy waves) released by an earthquake. S-waves travel through the Earth and are second to arrive at a seismograph station. Traveling at a speed of 4-7 kilometers per second, they travel slower than P-waves.

swells – Low, broad, rounded waves which can travel for hundreds of miles without losing much energy.

syncline – A downwardly arched fold. When eroded, the center beds (axis beds) are younger than the beds to either side.

system – The group of rocks formed during a particular geological time period.

talc – A very soft, white or green mineral, ranking #1 on the Mohs scale of hardness. It is a magnesium-rich silicate often formed from the alteration of ultramafic rocks.

tectonics – The creation of folds and faults due to directed pressure or stress.

tectonic plates – See **plates**.

terminus – The downhill end of a glacier.

Tertiary – The earliest of the two periods of the Cenozoic Era, lasting from 66 to 1.6 million years ago. (For the origin of the name, see **Quaternary**.)

texture – The size and shape of the grains in a rock.

thermal expansion and contraction – The mechanical weathering of rocks at the Earth's surface by a heating (expansion) and cooling (contraction) cycle.

thrust fault – A dip-slip fault in which the hanging wall block of the fault moves down relative to the footwall block. Usually the fault plane is less than 45°.

topography – The shape of the land surface.

topset bed – See **delta**.

transform plate boundary – Area where two or more plates are moving laterally (sideways) past each other.

trellis drainage system – Drainage system in which streams follow valleys, and the smaller streams join them at right angles from the surrounding hillsides.

trench – The area where one plate is subducted under another.

Triassic – The earliest period in the Mesozoic Era, lasting from 245 to 208 million years ago. Named after the three-fold division of this period first determined in Germany.

tributary – Smaller stream that feeds into a larger one.

trough – Bottom of a wave.

trunk stream – The principle stream in a drainage system.

tuff – Consolidated pyroclastic material.

GLOSSARY

turbidite environments - Deposits on underwater marine slopes (continental slopes).

ultramafic – An igneous rock, magma, or lava with a composition that has less than 45% silica, and is rich in iron (Fe) and magnesium (Mg). Ultramafic minerals are dark in color.

unconformity – A gap in the rock sequence of a particular locality.

uniformitarianism – The assumption that the geological processes we see today operated in a similar way in the past.

uplift – A force that raises a sequence of rock, often due to stress or buoyancy.

unloading – See **exfoliation**.

U-shaped valley – Typical shape of a valley carved out by a glacier.

valley glacier – Small glaciers confined within mountain valleys.

velocity – Speed given in distance divided by time, such as miles per hour or kilometers per second.

volcano – A vent in the surface of the Earth through which magma and pyroclastic fragments erupt.

volcanic edifice – The physical structure of a volcano.

volcanic igneous rock – Rock formed from lava or pyroclastic material on the Earth's surface. Also called "intrusive igneous rock." Named after Vulcan, the Roman god of fire.

V-shaped valley – Typical shape of a valley carved by a stream.

wave – The up-and-down movement of water due to an oscillatory movement of water molecules.

wavelength – The distance from one wave crest to the next.

weathering – The physical disintegration and chemical alteration of rocks on the Earth's surface.

wave refraction – The behavior of a wave that slows down and bends in a direction more parallel to the shore.

welded tuff – Rock formed from pyroclastic materials so hot that the materials fused together.

Personal Notes

STUDY SIDEKICK

I hate quotations.

– Ralph Waldo Emerson